The BTO/CJ Garden BirdWatch Book

by Mike Toms

Dedicated to the memory of Chris Mead

Published by The British Trust for Ornithology

British Trust for Ornithology
The Nunnery
Thetford
Norfolk
IP24 2PU
01842–750050
www.bto.org

First published in 2003

© 2003, British Trust for Ornithology, Thetford

ISBN 1–902576–73–X

Text: Mike Toms
Design & layout: Mike Toms
Printed by Reflex Litho, St Helen's Way, Thetford, IP24 1HG

Front cover: Blackbird by Tommy Holden. Title Page: Bullfinch by Tommy Holden.

CONTENTS

FOREWORD

For many decades, gardens and garden birds were regarded as having little value in the conservation and scientific scene. How things have changed! Because of the effects of the Common Agricultural Policy, intensification of agriculture, urbanisation and pollution, many of our once common garden birds have declined. This is largely due to depletion of natural food resources. Unless action is taken there is a risk of some of them becoming extinct. Hopefully this will not happen.

Fortunately garden bird feeding has changed dramatically over the last 15 years. The introduction of new, wholesome foods and feeding systems has enabled all-year-round feeding to be carried out. A greater understanding of birds' dietary requirements has led to much more suitable and safer foods becoming available. This – coupled with the huge increase in the general public's awareness of what they can do to help 'their' birds – is beginning to make a difference.

Feeding garden birds should have two primary objectives. Firstly to assist birds through the natural crisis points in their life cycle and secondly to help redress the balance of what we have done to the wider countryside. Bird feeding has increased five-fold in the last fifteen years. In early days we could help approximately 18 species in the winter. Now we can help 80 species throughout the year. What effect this is having you will see in later pages. Mike Toms and the Garden BirdWatch team have produced an enthralling book, showing how things have changed for the better since the scheme started in 1995.

Hopefully this book will encourage more of you to take part in what is turning out to be the largest and most successful year-round garden bird survey in the World. The results being produced are vital to our understanding of our garden birds and the factors affecting their survival.

Chris. J. Whittles

Chris Whittles
Chairman, CJ WildBird Foods

ACKNOWLEDGEMENTS

This book would not have been possible without the kindness, dedication and efforts of a great many people. First and foremost, there are the thousands of Garden BirdWatchers past and present who have contributed to the BTO/CJ Garden BirdWatch project, both financially and through their weekly recording of garden birds. Their observations, questions and photographs have made running the Garden BirdWatch project a privilege for me and for my two predecessors, Andrew Canon and Derek Toomer. The Garden BirdWatch project is further supported by CJ WildBird Foods, whose Chairman, Chris Whittles, had the foresight to see that the project would be successful, and the generosity to invest in its future. Along with Nigel Clark and the late Chris Mead, to whom this book is dedicated, Chris Whittles got this project up and running.

Garden BirdWatch is very much a team effort and working with me here at the Nunnery are Margaret Askew, Carol Povey, Jacky Prior and Rosie Cleary, all of whom put a great deal of time and effort into the smooth operation of the project. Dawn Balmer, Peter Beaven and Su Gough have helped to answer queries about garden birds. We are also supported by a number of volunteers (staff, relatives, local Garden BirdWatchers and others) who kindly give up their spare time to help, and other staff who share an office with us and who, along with our receptionists, provide much-needed support when we are swamped by Garden BirdWatch mail. I am very grateful to all of them.

Many people were involved in the production of this book, helping in different ways to turn it from idea into reality. Graham Appleton and David Glue helped with early drafts and shared their knowledge with me, advising on what to cut and what was missing. Dawn Balmer, Peter Beaven, Nigel Clark, Jenny Gill, Su Gough, Helen Kramer, Martin George, Peter Lack, Dave Leech, Carol Povey, John Povey, Jacky Prior, Alic Prior, Lyn Toms and Derek Toomer proof-read the various sections, though if there are any mistakes these are likely to be my own. Members of the BTO's Publications Working Group advised on design considerations and James Mackinnon, Simon Gillings and Rob Robinson extracted data for many of the analyses, the results of which are presented in this book. Jeff Baker and Simon Gillings kindly produced the artwork and the wonderful photographs were kindly provided by Dawn Balmer, Margaret Barton, Derek Belsey, Phil Farrer, Darren Frost, Martin George, John Harding, George Higginbotham, Tommy Holden, Dick Jeeves, G Olioso, Jill Pakenham, Rosie Rees, Graham Roberts, Rob Robinson, John Tully, Richard Vaughan, Colin Varndell, David Waistell and Mike Weston. Thanks are also due to Andy and Alan at Reflex Litho who, as always, have done a tremendous job. The references made in this book to other BTO surveys would not have been possible were it not for the efforts of those volunteers and staff involved in such projects as the Nest Record Scheme, the Ringing Scheme, Migration Watch and the many monitoring and research projects coordinated by the BTO's Populations Department and Terrestrial Ecology Unit. The map on page 16 is reproduced from Gibbons, D.W. *et al.* (1993) *The New Atlas of Breeding Birds in Britain & Ireland.* and published by T. & A. D. Poyser, London.

In addition to the thanks I owe to those people I have already mentioned, I should also give special mention to the late Chris Mead, whose enthusiasm for Garden BirdWatch and garden birdwatchers has had a big influence on me; to my parents who have always supported my interest in natural history and to my wife, Lyn, who is so accepting of the time that my interest in birds seems to occupy. Thank you all!

Mike Toms
Garden BirdWatch Organiser

Gardens for birds

*Great Spotted Woodpecker
by George Higginbotham*

Gardens provide important habitat for many bird species, supporting some individuals that are present year-round and others that only visit when food is in short supply in other habitats. An appreciation of how and when birds use gardens can make an important contribution to our understanding of the pressures faced by different species as they respond to changes within the wider countryside.

Gardens are important

We already know, from research carried out by British Trust for Ornithology (BTO) volunteers and staff, that gardens and the food we provide within them, can have a very positive influence on wild bird populations. Such research has shown, for instance, that farmland birds like Goldfinch and Yellowhammer markedly increased their use of garden food resources at a time when their farmland populations were in difficulty. Does this then mean that garden bird feeding buffers bird populations against the declines taking place within the wider countryside? It may well do but, whether or not this proves to be the case, there are other ways in which the use of gardens by birds is of great conservation value.

As the wildlife gardening enthusiast Chris Baines notes in his book; wildlife gardening "*most importantly brings so many people face to face with nature on a daily basis.*" For people to witness wildlife (usually birds) at close quarters and from the comfort

Gardens as green oases by Mike Toms

of their own homes, greatly adds to the appreciation of the diversity of life which lives beyond our windows, especially when many people lack the opportunity to interact with wildlife in the countryside.

Many of the issues pertaining to garden wildlife (like the problems of introduced species, potential conflicts between predators and their prey or the impacts of disease or human behaviour) have parallels within the wider environment. This means that any appreciation of these issues, that may come from watching and feeding garden wildlife, should increase our understanding of how other ecosystems work. Such understanding forms the basis of successful conservation.

Tree Sparrows by Tommy Holden

Backyard biodiversity

A recent MORI poll, conducted on behalf of the Royal Horticultural Society, indicated that 51% of gardeners put out food for birds or other wildlife and that 35% spent time watching wildlife within their gardens. Less than 1% of the species in our gardens are vertebrates, like birds and mammals, yet these eye-catching groups remain the most recognisable and are also the ones that attract the most interest. Gardens make a contribution to biodiversity and, while much of the species diversity for some groups (like plants) may be made up of non-native species, this diversity is still important. *Buddleja* may not be a native shrub but the nectar it produces is important to insects such as butterflies and hoverflies.

The retail value of the garden bird feeding industry is estimated to be worth some 150 to 180 million pounds, and the market is still increasing. It is the provision of this supplementary food which serves to attract much of our garden bird diversity, something that is possible because many birds are highly mobile and able to cross areas of unsuitable habitat in order to find food, nest sites or shelter. This provides the opportunity for farmland and woodland birds to move into gardens (especially rural ones) at those times of year when food is scarce within other habitats (see box below).

Gardens as a habitat for birds

Just how important are gardens for birds? There are virtually no bird species within Britain & Ireland that occur only within gardens, to the exclusion of all other habitat types, although one might argue that nesting Swifts and House Martins are limited to human habitats. However, gardens have been shown to support a large component of the populations of a number of breeding species, *e.g.* Blackbird, Starling and House Sparrow. The BTO Garden Nesting Survey, established by Richard Bland and John Tully and carried out by BTO Garden BirdWatchers, has emphasized that the size of breeding bird populations within gardens may be substantially greater than previously thought. For some species, such as Blackbird, populations exist at higher densities in gardens than in farmland and are more productive. For others, garden populations are less productive than their farmland or woodland counterparts.

Work carried out on garden mammals, by researchers at the University of Bristol, has shown that the chances of seeing a mammal species is much lower in gardens surrounded by other gardens, than in those surrounded by habitats like woodland or farmland. While mammals generally are less mobile than birds (and therefore more strongly influenced by surrounding habitats) this fact, coupled with information gathered on bird productivity, suggests that the garden habitat in itself is not as suitable for many species as other natural and semi-natural habitats (See Great Tit example overleaf).

Do farmland birds use gardens in winter?

In recent winters, BTO volunteers have been carrying out 'Winter Walks' to identify the patterns of abundance, distribution and habitat use for a range of farmland bird species. The resulting reporting rate graphs are similar to those used in Garden BirdWatch, and show the seasonal patterns of occurrence in farmland.

For a number of species, these graphs show that, as the winter progresses, so the reporting rate falls. Over the same period, the Garden BirdWatch reporting rates increase, showing birds moving into gardens.

This suggests that species like Goldfinches and Greenfinches move out of farmland as their natural food supplies become depleted, bringing them increasingly into gardens. We hope that future BTO research, especially bird ringing, will help us to understand how and why individual birds switch habitats.

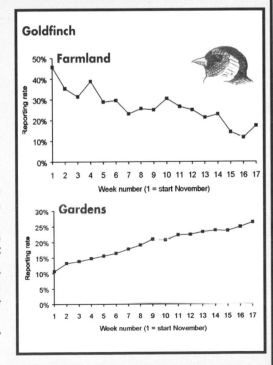

Goldfinch

Great Tit breeding success - costs and benefits

Great Tit breeding success in gardens has been shown to be lower than that in woodland, a consequence of the greatly reduced availability of insect food in most gardens. Yet overwinter survival rates are higher in gardens because of the supplementary food we make available. The presence of this food actually attracts Great Tits into gardens from nearby woodland during late autumn and winter, especially in those years when woodland seed supplies are low. So Great Tits using gardens in winter may increase their chances of survival over those that remain within woodland.

Great Tit by David Waistell

However, those Great Tits that do remain in woodland, and which manage to survive the winter, are more likely to claim the available territories than those that have wintered elsewhere. This means that some of those Great Tits wintering in gardens will be unable to secure a breeding territory in the best breeding habitat and may be forced to breed in the less suitable garden environment.

This highlights how complex natural systems are, and how the importance of gardens for bird populations is not necessarily something that can readily be calculated.

Variations between gardens

All gardens are not equal. The bird community of a city centre garden will be very different from that of a large rural property or a suburban semi. Such differences occur for a number of reasons. Some are due to the nature of the garden, while others are the result of factors operating at a wider spatial scale (*e.g.* geographic location or nearby habitats).

Within Britain & Ireland, there is a southeast/northwest gradient to the numbers of bird species to be found. The southeast supports a wider range of species than the northwest, something that is related to our position relative to the Continent, but also influenced by the distribution of soil types and habitats. Of course, there are species that are only found in the northern and western parts of Britain & Ireland and some of these feature in gardens on a regular basis.

Local features, like the habitats surrounding a particular garden, will also have an influence on the species present. An analysis of the Garden BirdWatch dataset has shown that the likelihood of many species occurring in gardens is more dependent upon the nature of the surrounding habitat rather than on features within the garden itself. A rural garden surrounded by arable farmland will be much more likely to feature birds such as Yellowhammer and Reed Bunting in winter than a garden in countryside where grassland dominates. The presence of nearby woodland may increase the number of species using a garden at certain times of year but birds may leave to feed in the woodland when suitable fruits and seeds are available. Gardens situated right on the coast (especially the south and east coasts) are the ones most likely to turn up a rare migrant, seeking shelter after completing a long sea crossing. There are general patterns that can be teased out from the Garden BirdWatch data, when they are analysed by the type of garden as defined by the Garden BirdWatchers themselves. For many species, such analyses show rural gardens to be better used than urban or suburban ones (*e.g.* Robin – see box opposite) but this is not always the case (*e.g.* House Sparrow).

Seasonality of use

The various species of birds to be found in gardens often show a distinct annual cycle. There are obvious patterns to the arrival and departure of summer migrants like House Martins or winter visitors like Redwing. In addition, many 'resident' species are not present in the garden for the whole year.

The Robin graph (right) shows that the greatest number of Garden BirdWatch gardens hold Robins during the winter months and that reporting rates are much lower during the breeding season. Many of the Robins present in winter in gardens must be breeding elsewhere during the summer, as you will see on pages 70–71.

Many species have their lowest reporting rates in late summer and early autumn, a time when there are abundant supplies of berries and seeds in farmland hedgerows or along railway embankments. The Garden BirdWatch Team receive lots of calls in October from worried birdwatchers wondering where all their birds have gone. Once these food resources have been depleted the birds will be back at bird feeders and tables.

Long-term trends

With all the changes that have occurred in the wider countryside over the past sixty or so years, it is likely that garden bird populations will have changed, both in terms of numbers and in terms of the range of species using gardens. Long-term monitoring projects, like the BTO's Garden BirdWatch and Garden Bird Feeding Survey, are a means by which the changing importance of gardens can be studied.

The introduction of new foods and feeding techniques has enabled some species to increase their use of gardens, while long-term declines in other species may result from problems in other habitats. By monitoring garden birds, their productivity and their populations we should be able to increase our understanding of the importance of gardens and be better placed to implement effective conservation strategies.

Garden Robins

The average Garden BirdWatch reporting rate for Robins differs between habitats, being highest in rural gardens and lowest in urban habitats. In addition, note how the reporting rate falls most dramatically in urban and suburban gardens during the breeding season - these gardens may support Robins in the winter but do not have enough resources to support breeding.

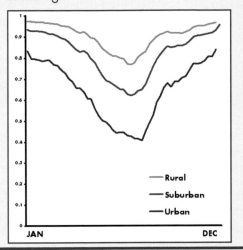

House Sparrow decline

The long term decline of House Sparrows can be seen from Garden Bird Feeding Survey records. Populations of House Sparrows using suburban and rural gardens have been in steady decline since the mid-1980s. Knowing when the decline began may help us to establish its cause and implement a conservation strategy.

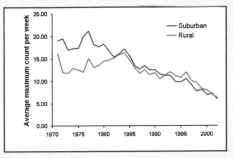

Wildlife-friendly gardening

It has often been said that we are a nation of gardeners, and the current level of interest in gardening programmes and horticultural shows bear testament to this. However, not all of us are gardeners, nor do we all have gardens. Having a garden (and taking an interest in it) is something which is likely to be determined by where you live, how old you are and how much you earn. Such factors also shape the style of garden you have and how you use it. This means that there are many different types of gardens, ranging in size from small to large and in character from formal to wilderness. Many gardens share similar features, often defined by what is in fashion and producing a recognisable style. Certain styles may be more wildlife-friendly than others, though pretty much every style will provide some wildlife benefit.

Until recently, a typical wildlife garden would have contained too much 'wildlife' and not enough 'garden' for many peoples' tastes but, increasingly, celebrity gardeners have shown how to incorporate some of the features of natural habitats into a more conventional garden. Such features may be small-scale (a few berry-producing shrubs or a pond) but others can take up large areas, such as with naturalistic planting schemes. The net result has been to make wildlife gardening an increasingly acceptable component of garden design and to show us the ways in which we can 'green the edges' of our gardens.

Welcoming wildlife

'Wildlife-friendly gardening' is perhaps a more appropriate term than 'wildlife gardening' because it encompasses all aspects of the gardening process. Using peat-free compost is wildlife-friendly because it helps protect the rich wildlife of our peat bogs, yet it has very little impact on the wildlife within our gardens. Increasing the wildlife value of a garden requires a change of emphasis and a move towards a more organic approach to garden management. Yet this change of emphasis does not require a fundamental shift in attitude, since it is perfectly possible to

introduce simple elements that significantly improve the whole garden for wildlife, without reducing its beauty or function.

The important thing, when welcoming wildlife into a garden, is to introduce features that are relevant to its size, location, soil type and style. Central to this is planning; finding out which animals you are likely to attract and which plants will work best for you. By doing so, it should be possible to create a garden that is rich in wildlife yet still provides enjoyment to all members of the household.

Hoverfly on flower by Mike Toms

The integration of features in this way may not produce a garden that is perfect for wildlife, but should be an improvement on what was there previously. It is also more likely to find favour with gardeners than a more radical change. This means that many more gardens could contain at least some wildlife-friendly components, something which should have benefits at both local and national levels.

A recent statistic, published by the Department for Environment, Food and Rural Affairs, highlights the problem we face – new houses are being built on greenfield sites at a density of 22 houses per hectare. This means that, as individuals, we have very little land under our direct control and it is only by working together that we can make a difference.

Putting together a garden

Later pages in this section of the book will deal with attracting birds and making a garden more bird-friendly, leaving these first few pages to other aspects of wildlife-friendly gardening.

Plants and plantings

Plants are usually the central focus of a garden, providing both the backdrop and detail used to please the senses. Within a wildlife-friendly garden the plants serve another function, providing cover and feeding opportunities for a range of animal species. It is well known that native species of plant generally support a more diverse community of animals than non-native species, simply because the two groups have existed alongside one another for many generations and have developed complex relationships. Having said this, many introduced species of plants can support a diverse community of other organisms and are valuable additions to any garden.

A species of native plant may also be established in a garden for the simple reason that it is under threat in the wider countryside. Many species of annual 'weeds', once commonly found in arable fields, are now scarce within the farmed environment but could be grown in a garden. These include colourful species like corncockle, pheasant's eye, corn marigold and corn poppy. Planting native species, perhaps by establishing a wildflower meadow, needs careful thought and is generally not easy to do. Seeds need to be sourced from reputable suppliers and should not contain imported or unsuitable material. Meadows (I use the term loosely since one might only be covering an area a few metres square) can be hard to get going and it can be difficult to maintain a diverse sward. Different species within the sward may flower at different times of the year, so it is important to plan the type of meadow one wishes to achieve. Summer-flowering meadows should be cut once, typically in August, after the flowers have produced their seed. Spring-flowering meadows require two cuts (one in early June and one in early autumn). In both cases, it is important to remove the clippings to maintain the low nutrient status favoured by many of these plants.

Particular species of plants can be selected to attract specific insects (see box below). Some plants are particularly attractive to butterflies and moths, others to

---

Plants for attracting insects

Many different plants can be used to attract insects to a garden. Choose those that fit in with your growing conditions.

African marigold – *Tagetes erecta*	Hawthorn – *Crataegus monogyna*
Bell heather – *Erica cinerea*	Heliotrope – *Heliotropium arborescens*
Borage – *Borago officinalis*	Ivy – *Hedera helix*
Butterfly bush – *Buddleja davidii*	Lady's bedstraw – *Galium verum*
Californian lilac – *Ceanothus impressus*	Lady's smock – *Cardamine pratensis*
China aster – *Callistephus chinensis*	Lavender – *Lavandula angustifolia*
Cornflower – *Centaurea cyanus*	Michaelmas daisy – *Aster novi-belgii*
Corn marigold – *Chrysanthemum segetum*	Night-scented stock – *Matthiola bicornis*
Elder – *Sambucus nigra*	Ox-eye daisy – *Leucanthemum vulgare*
Evening primrose – *Oenothera biennis*	Snapdragon – *Antirrhinum majus*
Fleabane – *Erigeron speciosus*	White dead nettle – *Lamium album*
Foxglove – *Digitalis purpurea*	Winter aconite – *Eranthis hyemalis*
Globe thistle – *Echinops ritro*	
Grape hyacinth – *Muscari armeniacum*	

Left – Ruby Tiger. Right – a Platycheirus hoverfly. By Mike Toms

bees and hoverflies and others still to birds and mammals. Try to incorporate a range of plants, including some that flower early in the year (like primrose, wood anemone and winter aconite) to provide a source of nectar for early flying insects, and think about where you are planting them. Plants placed in sunny, sheltered spots are more likely to be visited by hoverflies and bees than those in more exposed locations. Clumps or groups of plants will be more attractive than single plants scattered throughout the garden. It is not just flowers that are important but also fruit, seeds and the plant itself, all of which are utilised by a range of species.

Creating a pond

A pond can be one of the most attractive features of a wildlife-friendly garden. It is also one of the easiest features to establish (admittedly with a bit of hard graft to dig it out) and can be particularly rewarding. To an extent, size matters. The bigger (and deeper) the better, but even a small pond can make a difference to the wildlife value of a garden. Bigger ponds are better because they have a more stable temperature, can support more species and are less likely to suffer from algal blooms. A good size would be 3 metres long by 1.5 metres wide and about 0.75 metre deep at the deepest point. Ensure that it has some shallow margins and gently sloping sides, allowing access to wildlife that may come to bathe or drink from the pond. Try to make the pond blend into the landscape. Not only does this make the pond more appealing visually but it also allows wildlife to enter and leave the pond without attracting the unwanted attentions of predatory cats or birds.

The pond itself can be constructed from a pre-moulded plastic or fibreglass shell, clay, concrete or with a flexible liner. One constructed from concrete needs to be 'seasoned' before planting up, since chemicals released from the concrete may be harmful to plants and other wildlife. Flexible liners may be damaged by sharp stones or the claws of pets so care is needed where they are used.

The BTO wildlife pond by Mike Toms

Plants for ponds

Try to establish plenty of plants in and around the pond. Native ones are best, especially as we have lots of wonderful native species to choose from.

Bogbean – *Menyanthes trifoliata*
Curled pondweed – *Potamogeton crispus*
Sharp-flowered rush – *Juncus acutiflorus*
Rigid hornwort – *Ceratophyllum demersum*
Marsh marigold – *Caltha palustris*
Meadowsweet – *Filipendula ulmaria*
Purple loosestrife – *Lythrum salicaria*
Ragged robin – *Lychnis flos-cuculi*
Lesser spearwort – *Ranunculus flammula*
Spiked water-milfoil – *Myriophyllum spicatum*
Water-plantain – *Alisma plantago-aquatica*
Common water starwort – *Callitriche stagnalis*
Yellow iris – *Iris pseudacorus*

Fringed Lily by Mike Toms

Ponds are particularly attractive to small children so do remember to take sensible precautions if needed. Once the pond has been established and planted with suitable plants (see box), you will soon find that wildlife moves in of its own accord. If you have managed to get the right balance of plants and nutrients, the pond should need little in the way of day-to-day management. If it needs topping up in the summer, ideally use rainwater from a water butt. If you have to use tap water, then let it stand for 48 hours before adding it. The most serious problem likely to be encountered is an algal bloom, something that can often be controlled by using pads of barley straw, added to the pond in spring and autumn. Chemicals released from the barley straw, as it breaks down, inhibit the algae's reproductive cycle.

Garden lawns

One of the most important, but undervalued, part of any garden is the lawn. It can take many forms, from formal stripes to a full-blown meadow. A weed free, manicured lawn will not support the range of wildlife that a wildflower meadow does but it is possible to increase the value of a lawn by establishing some wildflowers in part of it.

Garden chemicals

One of the best ways in which to help maintain the quality of your wildlife-friendly garden is to avoid using chemicals to control weeds and invertebrate pests. A typical garden may contain several thousand species of invertebrates but only a handful of these will be harmful to plants or crops. Sprays tend to be indiscriminate in terms of the range of species they target and beneficial invertebrates may suffer. Fortunately, there are alternative methods to control or reduce the impacts of pests and diseases, including companion planting, biological control and by encouraging natural predators like hoverflies, lacewings and carabid beetles.

Compost and recycling

There are many other ways in which a garden can be made more wildlife-friendly. Compost produced from garden waste makes a much better mulch than peat, reduces waste and is better for the environment. Thought should also be given to other aspects of the garden, such as the wood used for decking or fencing, or the stone used for garden rockeries. The use of certain products can have an impact at sites far-removed from the garden and many resources are non-renewable. Of course, each gardener needs to find his/her own level, weighing up the costs of using particular materials or the impact of specific management practices. Developing a wildlife-friendly garden can mean many different things but the underlying result should mean that wildlife benefits.

Attracting garden birds

Different gardens attract different birds, depending upon geographical location and local habitats. An open garden in Surrey may be visited by a Green Woodpecker but in North Wales a Raven is more likely. Similarly, a suburban garden near an old railway line is more likely to be visited by a young Whitethroat than one in the middle of an estate. Although moving the position of one's garden is not usually possible, it is easy to provide shelter, food and nesting opportunities to increase your species list.

The available 'species pool'

The number of bird species that make up a particular bird community, known as 'species richness', shows geographical variation across Britain and Ireland. The greatest levels of species richness during the breeding season occur in the southeast and decline as one moves further north and west (see map). Species richness also varies seasonally, with the arrival of migrants from other regions. These summer and winter visitors show different geographical patterns to their settlement, again influencing the local species pool. Many of the summer migrants breed in the southern half of Britain and Ireland and only make it further north and west in smaller numbers, or not at all.

Goldfinch by Tommy Holden

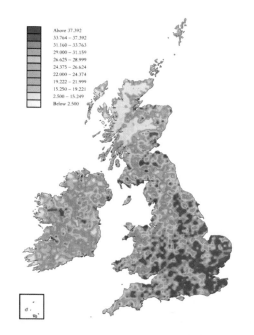

Geographical variation in species richness. BTO New Breeding Atlas.

Above 37.392
33.764 – 37.392
31.160 – 33.763
29.000 – 31.159
26.625 – 28.999
24.375 – 26.624
22.000 – 24.374
19.222 – 21.999
15.250 – 19.221
2.500 – 15.249
Below 2.500

The position of the garden in relation to surrounding habitats is particularly relevant in the case of those species that only make use of gardens at certain times of the year, notably during late winter, when feeding opportunities elsewhere are limited. Rural gardens tend to be the ones used by farmland species, like many of the finches, while those near to woodland are more likely to have visiting Jays, Great Spotted Woodpeckers and Treecreepers. Examination of the Garden BirdWatch dataset, with regard to how individual gardens are classified (urban, suburban or rural), has revealed some significant associations between particular species and garden type. Species like Starling, House Sparrow, Magpie, Feral Pigeon and Black-headed Gull are more likely to occur in urban gardens than in suburban or rural ones. These are adaptable birds, able to exploit the opportunities that may arise within the built-up environment.

Factors operating within the garden

Most birds visiting a garden will be looking for habitat features that are similar to those present in other 'natural' habitats, e.g. cover from predators, perches from which they can sing and suitable foods. Many gardens will have some of these features but only the largest gardens may have the space to hold the diversity of habitat structure favoured by the greatest number of species. Most of our gardens do not have the large trees and areas of dense scrub in which birds can support themselves for a whole year, which means that species other than Blackbirds and Robins will desert us for one or more seasons. The design of gardens and the facilities we provide can increase the number of residents and visitors.

Greenfinch by Tommy Holdén

The feeding ecology of different species influences which birds are able to utilise the garden environment. The lack of dense cover, range of plant species presented and the use of pesticides often means that the garden habitat supports relatively low numbers of insects, spiders and other invertebrates. In turn, this reduces the suitability of the garden habitat for insectivorous birds like warblers. Those species most commonly reported from gardens are ones that either tend to feed on seeds (*e.g.* finches) or are omnivorous (*e.g.* Blackbird). The types of foods these species require match those typically supplied by Man (*e.g.* black sunflower seed, peanuts, mixed seed and kitchen scraps). Examination

of the Garden BirdWatch dataset shows that the occurrence of 24 of the main Garden BirdWatch species is significantly higher in gardens where feeding takes place. All but one of these species feed directly on the food we provide, the remaining species being Sparrowhawk, which is attracted by the abundance of small birds.

One of the most important components of a bird-friendly garden is the provision of clean water. Birds require water for drinking and bathing throughout the year. However, it is during the summer months, when other water sources may be scarce, that a garden pond or bird bath really comes into its own. Moving water, or the sound of water dripping into a bird bath, seem particularly attractive.

The previous section on wildlife-friendly gardening highlights the range of opportunities for designing and managing a garden for birds and other wildlife. The establishment of cover, promotion of insect numbers and provision of water all go some way to introducing those elements of 'natural' communities that birds will respond to. There are three other important aspects that are sufficiently important to require their own sections – these are the provision of food (pages 18–20), hygiene (page 21) and nesting opportunities (pages 22–23).

Great Spotted Woodpecker by Derek Belsey

Foods and feeding

The modern approach to garden bird feeding is to use a range of foods that meet the specific nutritional requirements of a wide range of species over the course of the whole year. The traditional approach, of just providing bread, fats, peanuts and a few kitchen scraps, and largely limited to the winter, is increasingly losing favour, as garden birdwatchers make better use of new foods. Most small birds need to consume as much as 30% of their own bodyweight in food every day, just to maintain themselves. Feeding modern, high quality and oil-rich foods offers the best opportunity to provide birds with the energy and nutrients they require.

Does feeding make a difference?

There is a wealth of scientific evidence demonstrating that the provision of supplementary food can make a real difference to birds. Supplementary feeding has been shown to increase overwinter survival and productivity in a range of species (see box). Although much of this work has been on bird populations in habitats other than gardens, the same principles apply.

Most of the bird species that use gardens are limited by food availability – something that may be particularly apparent both during the breeding season and in winter. The provision of supplementary foodstuffs that exactly mirror what would normally be taken by the species, allows the garden birdwatcher to positively influence the productivity and survival of a range of bird species.

Late spring and summer feeding

Both the BTO and the RSPB advocate the provision of appropriate foods throughout the year, and not just in winter. During late spring and the breeding season, the adults of garden-breeding species may find it difficult to locate sufficient food to feed both themselves and their chicks, making supplementary feeding particularly important.

In many species, chicks require invertebrate food to develop properly. Adult birds utilise supplementary sunflower seeds and peanut granules while feeding all the insects they can find to their young. Although adult birds are able to differentiate between different types of food, and to select the appropriate food for their young, some studies have revealed that they will also deliver food provided at local bird tables to the nest. The evidence suggests, in Great Tits and Blue Tits at least, that the parent birds feed their chicks on the supplementary foods when favoured chick foods (*i.e.* small insects) are in short supply. This means that

Winter feeding

Various studies have shown that populations of Great Tits within woodland tend to fluctuate in parallel with the size of the beech mast crop; beech mast being an important winter food for this species. This suggests that the availability of winter food may determine the size of the breeding population the following year, through its effect on overwinter survival. Hans Källander, working in Sweden, tested the importance of overwinter food availability through a carefully controlled experiment. Supplementary food (in the form of sunflower seeds) was provided at a number of sites. The size of the breeding population in the following year at these sites was then calculated and compared with that at other sites at which supplementary food was not provided. The results of the experiment did indeed show that the provision of supplementary food

led to a larger breeding population the following year. Additionally, the increase in the breeding population was greater in those years when the winter weather was particularly severe and the beech mast crop was small. This suggests that supplementary feeding is particularly important when natural levels of food are low.

Great Tit by Tommy Holden

consideration needs to be given to which foods are provided within the breeding season. Live foods, like mealworms, are an obvious choice, while whole loose peanuts (which could choke young chicks) should be avoided. Although more work is needed to establish how summer feeding influences productivity, there is no doubt that it has a tremendous potential to benefit species that are normally less productive in garden habitats because of the lower availability of 'natural' foods.

Where to feed

Supplementary food can be provided in many ways, depending upon the type of food being used and the species for which it is intended. Different species are adapted to feeding on a range of foods and have clear preferences in how they obtain their food. Some species are primarily ground feeders (*e.g.* Robin, Dunnock and Blackbird) while others prefer to feed from hanging feeders (*e.g.* Great Tit, Blue Tit, Great Spotted Woodpecker and Siskin).

It is sensible to place hanging feeders and raised bird tables close to high cover, so that feeding birds can shelter in the bushes if a Sparrowhawk appears. Conversely, the best place for a ground feeding station is away from low vegetation, reducing the danger from cats, waiting to pounce. Birds balance the benefits of feeding on a particular feeder against the risks of attack from a predator. Dominant adult Great Tits have been shown to preferentially feed on feeders close to cover, pushing less dominant individuals onto more exposed feeders, where the risk of Sparrowhawk predation is greater.

Types of feeders and what to feed

Hanging bird feeders come in two main forms, one for seed and the other for peanuts. The choice of an appropriate design can be geared to local conditions. Some cage-feeders are designed to only provide access to smaller birds and these are an obvious choice where Feral Pigeons, Woodpigeons or squirrels are a nuisance. Similar cages are available for use on bird tables or at ground feeding stations. Starlings and Great Spotted Woodpeckers can sometimes get their tongues or feet caught in the mesh of red nut bags or green fat ball bags, so try to use a feeder with a rigid mesh. The diversity of feeders and tables offers the garden birdwatcher plenty of opportunity to develop a garden feeding station that benefits a wide range of species, feeding in many different ways.

Seeds tend to attract and support a wider range of species than straight peanuts and many garden birdwatchers use black sunflower seeds or sunflower hearts as their staple foods. Alongside these, quality peanuts that are endorsed by a wildlife body such as the BTO, BirdCare Standards Association or RSPB (and thus tested for a naturally occurring poison called aflatoxin), nyjer seed and high-energy seed mixes are equally valuable (see over). There are other foods, *e.g.* sultanas, that are good for ground-feeding Blackbirds and Song Thrushes, while pinhead oats are ideal for fine-billed Dunnocks. Finely grated cheese and windfall apples can be very useful, particularly in winter, while peanut cake, a mix of vegetable fats and peanut flour, is good for species like Long-tailed Tit and Nuthatch.

Long-tailed Tits by Dick Jeeves

Among the wide range of foods that can be put out for birds, there are five that deserve special attention, being the most widely used by garden birdwatchers. By providing a combination of foods it is possible to attract a wide range of species to your garden.

Peanuts

Peanuts are high in the oils and proteins needed by birds and have been used for many years at garden feeding stations. Always buy good quality peanuts from a reputable source and avoid those that show signs of mould. Peanuts are best supplied behind a mesh, so that a bird cannot take a whole peanut away (see text). Peanuts can also be supplied as granules or peanut cake.

Black sunflower seed

First introduced in the early 1990s, this seed revolutionised bird feeding, by providing a high energy food in a readily accessible form. These seeds feature in many table seed mixes but can also be presented on their own in hanging seed feeders. They are a favourite of Greenfinches and tits, although they may be shunned if sunflower hearts are available.

Sunflower hearts

Although more expensive than the black sunflower seeds from which these hearts are produced, they have two advantages. First, the birds can feed more quickly because they do not have to remove the husk. Second, the lack of a husk means that there are no unsightly piles of husks that typically appear under hanging seed feeders containing black sunflower seed.

Nyjer seed

A relatively new introduction to the bird feeding market and one that has found favour with Goldfinches, which seem to like the small size of these seeds. Because they are so small, nyjer seeds need to be supplied in a specially adapted feeder. They are rich in oil and ideal for birds with bills delicate enough to deal with them. They can be mixed with other seed mixes or sprinkled on the ground for Dunnocks.

Seed mixes

There is a vast range of seed mixes available on the market and some are much better than others. Cheaper mixes often contain a high proportion of cereal and tend to attract pigeons. Better quality mixes are lower in cereal content and so are particularly suitable for finches, tits and buntings. The best quality mixes are carefully balanced to cater for a range of bird species and their differing nutritional requirements.

Photographs by CJ WildBird Foods

The simple provision of food is not enough on its own. Consideration also needs to be given to how the food is presented, such that it is not detrimental to the health of the birds being fed.

Wild birds are susceptible to a range of different diseases and these may be transmitted from one bird to another, or to other animals (*e.g.* pets, children and garden birdwatchers). It is therefore important to adopt appropriate standards of hygiene when providing food at bird tables and in hanging feeders. Birds can gather in large numbers at garden feeding stations, just as they do at naturally abundant food sources, and this may increase the chances of disease transmission. There are a number of sensible precautions that can be adopted to reduce the risk of disease transmission (see box), thus ensuring that the benefit of garden feeding is maximised.

Of the many diseases that wild birds may contract, there are a number of more commonly reported ones that are worth special mention. These include *Salmonella*, which appears to be a common cause of

House Sparrows by Richard Vaughan

epidemics among garden birds during the winter months. Greenfinches appear to be particularly susceptible to *Salmonella*; affected individuals appear lethargic and fluffed up. Another commonly reported disease is caused by a papillomavirus which causes warts on the legs of Chaffinches and Bramblings. These growths usually only form on one leg and range in size from a small nodule to a wart that engulfs the whole leg. Lameness sometimes occurs but it is thought that most individuals suffer only minor inconvenience.

Some sensible precautions

Ensure that you keep surfaces on which birds feed clean. Ideally, brush bird tables daily to clear away droppings.

If you feed on the ground, do not put food in the same place every day, moving the feeding area around regularly helps reduce the risk of disease transmission.

Provide food at several sites within the garden, so that large numbers of birds do not gather in the same place.

Move hanging feeders periodically and keep the area beneath them clear of droppings, spilt food and seed husks.

Clean bird tables and hanging feeders on a regular basis, ideally using a recognised cleaning agent designed for the purpose. Rinse feeders and tables thoroughly after cleaning and ensure they are dry before refilling with food.

Ensure that any water you provide is fresh, and that bird baths are cleaned and rinsed regularly.

Some bird diseases can be passed on to humans, so it essential that you should observe scrupulous personal hygiene.

Nests and nesting

Many gardens lack the range of nesting opportunities needed by birds for successful breeding. Therefore, the provision of artificial nest sites (typically nestboxes) within a garden can really help the local bird population. To be successful, artificial nest sites need to be of an appropriate design and erected in a suitable place. They should also be weatherproof, secure from nest predators and maintained in good condition.

Great Tit removing faecal sac by David Waistell

Other nesting opportunities can be created by planting trees and shrubs that will provide the cover needed for open nesters like Song Thrush and Blackbird. Hawthorn, cotoneaster, privet and other ornamental shrubs are ideal, as are climbing plants like ivy or virginia creeper. Small conifers or conifer hedges are often used, especially by Greenfinches, and these have the advantage of providing year-round cover and roosting opportunities.

Nestboxes – the right design

Nestboxes can be divided into three main types: the classic tit box, the open-fronted box and various specialist designs for species like Swift and House Martin. Tit boxes have a complete front panel with a round hole drilled into it. The size of the hole (and the size of the box) determines which species will use it. For smaller birds (*e.g.* tits, sparrows and Nuthatch) the box itself can be quite small, with a minimum internal floor dimension of 10cm by 10cm, but for larger species (*e.g.* Starling and Jackdaw) the box

needs to be proportionally bigger. For tit and sparrow species, the base of the box should be at least 12cm below the bottom of the entrance hole, so that predatory cats cannot reach the nest contents. Suggested hole sizes and box designs are given in the box on the opposite page.

In open-fronted boxes, the upper part of the front is cut away, favouring species that like to nest in more open situations (e.g. Robin and Pied Wagtail). An open-fronted design works for Spotted Flycatcher but, because this species likes to be able to see over the edge of the nest while incubating, only a short, 3cm tall, front panel is needed. On the other hand, the Wren favours an open-fronted box with only a 3–4cm gap between the front panel and the roof.

Building your own nestbox can be very rewarding and there are a number of good books on the subject which include cutting plans for a range of species. One of the best is that written by Chris du Feu, called 'The

Nest Recording

Since 1939, the British Trust for Ornithology has operated the Nest Record Scheme, to gather information on breeding ecology. Nest recorders make a number of visits to a nest to count the numbers of eggs and young and to record how the nesting attempt is progressing. The Nest Record Unit provides a set of guidelines which are designed to reduce the risk of any disturbance to the nesting birds. Data collected through the scheme have been used by BTO scientists to investigate the causes of population declines and to study the impacts of global climate change.

Anyone can fill in Nest Record Cards for birds they find nesting in their gardens, and by doing so they can make a valuable contribution to this project. For more information, please contact: Nest Record Scheme, BTO, The Nunnery, Thetford, Norfolk, IP24 2PU, phone 01842-750050, visit www.bto.org or email nest.records@bto.org.

BTO NestBox Guide' and published by the BTO. Use wood that is at least 15mm thick and suitable for use outside. A coat of wood preservative will help to prolong the life of the box. Only treat the outside of the box, since the long-term effects of preservaives on birds are unknown. Many people prefer to purchase a nestbox and there is a bewildering array of designs available in pet shops, garden centres and by mail order. Some are wholly inappropriate, such as those that combine a nest box with a bird table, and such designs should be avoided. Look for boxes that are well-made and whose dimensions meet the requirements of the bird species you are hoping to attract.

Robins by Derek Belsey

Placement and maintenance

Generally, the direction that a box faces makes little difference provided that it is sheltered from the prevailing wind and rain, and positioned away from strong sunlight. Within Britain and Ireland, the most favoured orientation is towards the north, through east to southeast. Use the available cover to help position the box away from the unwanted attentions of nest predators but ensure that there is a clear flight path in to

the box. Make sure that the box is fastened securely to a structure (a tree, wall or post) and that it is in a quiet spot, away from the unwelcome attentions of predators or children. Never place a nestbox adjacent to a bird table or any hanging feeders – the residents may suffer from undue disturbance and can spend too much time trying to defend the area around the box. More detailed guidelines are available in the BTO NestBox Guide. Boxes should be cleaned out in the autumn, when any chance of further broods is over. Cleaning out boxes reduces the build-up of nest parasites, like fleas, which remain in the old nest and await the arrival of the next year's brood.

Nestbox dimensions

Species	Type	Size	Hole	Notes
Blue Tit	T	S	25mm	
Great Tit	T	M	28mm	
Coal Tit	T	S	25mm	Slightly smaller hole may be used.
House Sparrow	T	M	32mm	Place several boxes together.
Tree Sparrow	T	M	28mm	Place several boxes together.
Nuthatch	T	M	32mm	
Starling	T	L	45mm	
Jackdaw	T	VL	150mm	
Robin	OF	S/M	–	Position within cover.
Wren	T/OF	S	30mm	
Pied Wagtail	OF	S	–	
Spotted Flycatcher	OF	S	–	Front panel only 30mm tall.

Type: T – tit box, OF – open-fronted. Size: S – small, M – medium, L – large, VL – very large. Hole: diameter of the hole.

Watching garden birds

Watching gardens birds can be an incredibly rewarding experience, and it is one of the main reasons why many people provide food for wild birds on a daily basis. To watch wildlife from the comfort of your own home often provides a great opportunity to see species that are significantly more wary when encountered in other habitats. It also allows greater insight into their behaviour and ecology.

The degree of interest that one takes in watching garden birds can be incredibly varied and for many observers there is pleasure in just watching the antics of feeding and nesting birds. For other garden birdwatchers, the level of interest is much greater and centres on knowing what the birds are doing and why they are doing it. This is where projects like the BTO/CJ Garden BirdWatch can provide extra stimulus, by encouraging observers to pay greater attention to what is going on in their gardens. Once this interest has been stimulated it can become a serious and time-consuming hobby!

One of the great attractions of watching garden birds is that it does not require lots of different equipment, nor does it necessitate a large amount of commitment or expense. The activities of birds utilising a bird table can be watched over breakfast, whilst washing-up or from the comfort of an armchair by the fire. Other than the various feeders, bird tables and nestboxes that can be used to attract the birds in the first place, all that is really needed is a pair of binoculars (and even these may not be essential) and a good field guide to help with identification. *The Collins Bird Guide* by Mullarney, Svensson, Zetterström and Grant (ISBN 0 00 219728 6) is one of the best current guides, with excellent pictures and very useful notes, highlighting the differences between similar species. It covers all of the species found in Britain and Europe, although the inclusion of species not normally found in Britain or Ireland may sometimes be confusing. A large format version is also available.

The use of a camera to record unusual garden visitors or behaviour can be very beneficial. Several pictures of rare species have been taken by fortunate Garden BirdWatchers with cameras at the ready. Such photographs can then be shown to county bird recorders, enabling the record to be accepted for county or national bird

What to look for in a pair of binoculars

Binoculars come in a wide range of shapes and sizes, not to mention prices. Between the two extremes, of very cheap but not very good and more expensive than you actually need, there are many models that will provide you with a lifetime of good service. When choosing a pair of binoculars, ensure that they are comfortable and fit your needs.

Binoculars are rated using two numbers, the magnification and the diameter of the main lenses. A pair of binoculars rated 8x30 have a magnification of times 8 and a lens diameter of 30mm. The quality of the image will depend, in part, on these two values. The bigger the magnification, the closer the image will appear but the smaller your overall view will be. The wider the diameter of the lenses, the more light will be

let in and the brighter the image will appear. The quality of the lenses is also important and a good quality pair of 8x30 may produce as clear an image as a cheap pair of 8x50. For general use, it is best to choose a pair of 8x30 or 8x40.

Photograph by Dawn Balmer

reports far more readily than would have otherwise been possible. Photographs can also be used to document unusual behaviour (*e.g.* a Wren sunbathing)

Wren by Margaret Barton

Some garden birds are quite secretive and may only reveal their presence through their song or calls. It is often more difficult to identify a bird based on its call or song than on sight but there are some very good sound recordings now available and compact discs or tapes of garden bird songs can be purchased from many suppliers. There are also specialist videos and DVDs to help with the identification of garden birds. One of the best is produced by BirdGuides (see Further Reading) and couples excellent footage with really useful notes on identification, behaviour and song.

What to look out for

One of the beauties of watching garden birds is that there always seems to be something going on, whether it is a Coal Tit taking sunflower hearts away from a feeder to store elsewhere, an aggressive encounter between two Greenfinches or a young Blue Tit begging for food from one of its parents.

Many of the behaviours exhibited by birds can be seen in the garden and it is worth looking out for different things at different times of the year. During spring, male Robins and Blackbirds will be setting up territories within most gardens. This often leads to aggressive encounters between territory holders and intruders. Robins can be particularly intolerant of intruders, attacking other Robins and even Dunnocks. If you are fortunate enough to have breeding

Dunnocks, then it is worth looking out for examples of their complex breeding system (see page 68) and amazing pre-mating behaviour.

During the autumn, many gardens go quiet (see page 11) as birds feed elsewhere or undergo moult. Moulting birds tend to skulk about but may be seen preening their new plumage. Autumn is also a time of year when many migrant birds are on the move and this is when rarities begin to turn up in gardens. Migrant warblers may appear, to feed on fruits, and some fortunate garden birdwatchers are visited by Wrynecks, the rarest of our woodpeckers. With the arrival of winter, most garden feeding stations become very busy places, as birds seek out the food needed to get them through the long winter nights. At this time of year, it can prove very interesting to watch the daily pattern of arrivals, with the various species appearing at different times each day (see pages 38–39). It is also during the winter months that small birds can be seen roosting together in bushes or in roosting pockets and nestboxes. It is quite a sight to see a succession of Wrens enter a nestbox late in the afternoon, only to emerge again the next morning. The same birds may use the box over many nights, all huddling together to keep warm.

Unusual behaviour may be seen at any time of year and that is part of the enjoyment of watching garden birds, not knowing what you may see next.

Blue Tits by Margaret Barton

Studying garden birds

With so many people interested in their garden birds, there is huge potential for carrying out the much-needed research into how and why birds use gardens, and how garden bird populations may change over time. The key to harnessing this army of garden birdwatchers is to design research projects that best fit the balance between the range of questions for which we need answers and the range of survey techniques available.

While municipal parks and botanical gardens may provide ideal study sites for the individual researcher, interested in particular aspects of breeding ecology or community structure, private gardens can be more difficult to work in. For a start, private gardens tend to be small and any birds using the garden are likely to range over several other gardens in the local area. This means that any attempt to study the local population of a given species will require access to a large number of gardens. Andrew Cannon, studying garden birds in Sheffield, estimates that there are 3,000 privately owned gardens in his 1-km square study site. Each of these individual gardens is likely to be managed in a slightly different way and this creates an additional complication for the researcher. It should not be surprising, therefore, that populations of garden birds have not often been the subject of detailed study, except within the larger units of municipal gardens and parks, habitats in which birds may behave differently.

It is fortunate then that it is possible to answer important questions about the behaviour and ecology of garden birds by involving householders, using their interest in garden wildlife and knowledge of their own gardens, to gather the information required. Tapping into the army of garden birdwatchers is possible, providing that the project is interesting and the record taking is not too onerous.

Garden birdwatchers have made many important contributions to garden bird research but perhaps the greatest contribution they can make comes from involvement in the systematic recording that forms the basis of long-term monitoring programmes like Garden BirdWatch and the Garden Bird Feeding Survey. Information on relative changes in bird populations can be used alongside that gathered from other sources, and for other habitats, to build up an overall picture of what is happening to bird populations within Britain and Ireland. This type of approach is known as Integrated Population Monitoring and has been widely used by the BTO to alert conservation bodies and government agencies to changes in the populations of wild birds.

The use of volunteers, as opposed to paid professionals, for large-scale projects is often referred to as 'citizen science'. Carefully planned and implemented citizen science projects produce very valuable scientific information but have sometimes been looked down upon by some parts of academia. This is unfortunate, because the citizen science approach provides a very powerful research tool, as long as contributors can give consistent answers to the questions posed.

Garden BirdWatch uses a set framework of instructions, producing a consistent pattern to the recording that takes place. There are differences between individual observers, in terms of their level of experience and commitment to the project, just as there are between individual paid professionals, but it is the consistency of recording by individuals that is important, allowing comparisons to be made from one week to the next. The effect of any differences between individuals is virtually removed by having a huge sample of people involved, such that individual mistakes have no influence on the underlying patterns revealed across the participants as a whole.

Fieldfare by Mike Toms

Many birds that use our gardens are not as common or familiar as one might think, and some are decidedly scarce. This fact only really captured public attention following the widespread media interest in the decline of the House Sparrow. Here was a species with a long association with Man, which had virtually disappeared from many of its former urban haunts, almost unnoticed. How could we have let this happen?

Those species that have adapted to live alongside us, have managed to find features within the man-made environment that closely match those they would normally rely on within their natural habitats. In the most adaptable species, the range of features that can be utilised is wider than that in more specialised, less-adaptable species. There are more opportunities in an urban centre for a House Sparrow than there are for a Swallow.

If the features required by a species are lost, perhaps by a change in building design or urban land-use, or the environment in which they live becomes more hostile, then this may affect the viability of these

House Sparrow by Mike Weston

populations within the urban or suburban habitat. This is what appears to be happening in the case of the House Sparrow. It follows, therefore, that while a particular species may be common at the moment it may become scarce if conditions change. The appearance of garden birds on the list of species of conservation concern reflects the fact that there are problems within the urban environment as well as elsewhere in the wider countryside.

Garden birds of conservation concern

Results from BTO surveys and monitoring programmes are used to review the status of the United Kingdom's bird populations and to highlight species which are of conservation concern. This approach results in the production of three lists, all published and reviewed on a regular basis. Birds on the 'Green list' are currently regarded as being of low conservation concern - *i.e.* there are no immediate threats to their populations. About 120 species currently appear on the 'Amber list' (medium conservation concern) because of the way in which their populations have changed or because their total population size is very small. These 'Amber list' species include garden birds like Mistle Thrush, Dunnock and Redwing. Those species of greatest concern are placed on the 'Red list', currently consisting of about 40 species, including House Sparrow, Starling, Yellowhammer, Willow Tit, Song Thrush, Spotted Flycatcher and Bullfinch, all of which have declined in number by half or more since 1970.

In addition to these lists, the UK Government uses breeding bird populations as one of their 15 headline indicators reflecting the quality of life within the United Kingdom. The breeding bird 'Quality of Life' indicator summarises information on the changing status of over 100 species, set up using the BTO's Common Birds Census. Since the Government has pledged to reverse the long-term declines in farmland and woodland birds, the indicator can be used to assess the success of their policies.

Starling by Colin Varndell

The Garden Bird Feeding Survey

The BTO's Garden Bird Feeding Survey (GBFS) is the longest running annual survey of garden birds anywhere in Europe, having been launched during the 1970/71 winter and currently involving about 250 participants annually. Although the project was originally set up to assess the range of birds using supplementary food provided in gardens throughout the winter months, and to examine feeding preferences, it also provides a very valuable check on how garden bird populations have changed over time. One of the most important aspects of the Garden Bird Feeding Survey is that throughout its 33–year run, observers have always used the same recording methodology, allowing comparisons to be made between years (see box).

The Garden Bird Feeding Survey involves weekly counts of those bird species using supplementary foods between October and March each year. Gardens included in the project are subdivided into those classed as 'rural' and those classed as 'suburban' in location – currently a roughly equal split across the 250+ sites. For each group of sites

Blue Tits by Tommy Holden

a number of different indices can be calculated that reflect the numbers and range of species visiting gardens during a particular winter. One of these is the Peak Count Index. Calculated separately for each species within each garden type, the Peak Count Index is a measure of the maximum number of individuals, of a particular species, seen together, averaged across all of the gardens within the garden type.

Garden Bird Feeding Survey results

Results from the Garden Bird Feeding Survey fall into two groups; those highlighting the effects of annual events (*e.g.* a very cold winter or an autumn with a large crop of beech mast) and those reflecting long-term changes in the size or behaviour of a bird population (*e.g.* increase in the use of gardens, decline in numbers across a range of habitats).

Annual effects

Some species show quite dramatic responses to annual effects, like the severity of the weather. Species like Fieldfare (see graph 1 in box), Pied Wagtail and Redwing may increase their use of gardens during particularly severe weather, while others, like Wren, Goldcrest and Long-tailed Tit may show reduced numbers in the year following a severe winter. Others, typically winter visitors like Brambling and Siskin but also residents like Coal Tit (see graph 2 in box),

Changing fortunes

The changing fortunes of different bird species can be seen by comparing the most recent GBFS figures with those from the 1970s.

Rank	Species	% of gardens 2002/03	1970s*
1	Robin	100.0	99
2	Blue Tit	99.6	99
3	Blackbird	99.2	99
4	Great Tit	98.1	93
5=	Chaffinch	97.0	92
5=	Greenfinch	97.0	92
7	Dunnock	96.2	95
8	Collared Dove	91.7	60
9	Coal Tit	87.9	70
10	House Sparrow	86.7	97
11	Starling	85.6	96
12	Magpie	72.7	29

* The 1970s figures are an average for the winters 1970/71 to 1979/80.

Great Tit and Nuthatch may respond to the availability of favoured food sources. The 'boom-bust' pattern of the beech mast crop may determine the degree to which individual species turn to garden feeding stations. In years when beech mast is widely available, the species that feed on it will be less frequent visitors to gardens.

Long-term trends

The long-term changes in the use of gardens, that may be caused by a shift in behaviour or by a change in population size, can be seen in the Garden Bird Feeding Survey results for several species. When viewed in isolation, such plots may not explain why a particular species has increased or decreased in its use of gardens but when other BTO datasets are also examined, a more complete picture typically begins to emerge.

The recovery of the Sparrowhawk population from the effects of organochlorine pesticides (see page 48) is visible in the Garden Bird Feeding Survey results (see graph 3 in box). The recovery occurred first in rural gardens but, as the population has increased, so the numbers visiting suburban gardens has also gone up. Interestingly, over the last few winters the increase has slowed, perhaps suggesting that some factor, such as nest site availability or food abundance, may be starting to limit Sparrowhawk numbers.

The most valuable contribution made by the Garden Bird Feeding Survey has been to alert conservationists to population declines in those bird species, like Starling (see graph 4 in box) and House Sparrow, with a large component of their breeding population located within the urban and suburban environment.

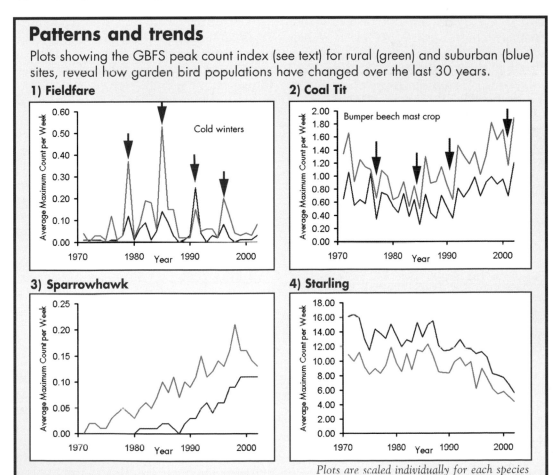

Patterns and trends

Plots showing the GBFS peak count index (see text) for rural (green) and suburban (blue) sites, reveal how garden bird populations have changed over the last 30 years.

1) Fieldfare

2) Coal Tit

3) Sparrowhawk

4) Starling

Plots are scaled individually for each species

For many people, the BTO/CJ Garden BirdWatch is simply an extension to the records they already keep of the birds using their gardens throughout the year. The structure of Garden BirdWatch, with its weekly recording format and consistent recording effort, greatly increases the scientific value of these observations. By gathering small amounts of simple information from a very large number of gardens, it is possible to answer some complex ecological questions about the relationships between individual bird species and the garden environment.

Some of the changes in garden bird populations are likely to reflect changes in the bird populations over a wider area. For example, as farmland habitats become less suitable for seed-eating birds during the winter months we see an increasing reliance on feeding stations within rural and suburban gardens. Although it is not clear how bird numbers reported in gardens relate to their absolute populations, the Garden BirdWatch results can be used alongside other BTO studies to examine how changes in populations of individual species differ across habitats.

Yellowhammer by Tommy Holden

History of Garden BirdWatch

The BTO/CJ Garden BirdWatch was launched in late 1994 in readiness for recording to begin in 1995. The idea behind the project came from discussions between Chris Mead and Nigel Clark of the BTO and Chris Whittles of CJ WildBird Foods.

Earlier attempts to monitor garden bird populations, such as the Garden Bird Enquiry, had always encountered the problem of funding the scheme for more than just a couple of years. What was needed was long-term funding. This problem was solved by making what was regarded at the time as a very brave decision – namely to ask participants in the scheme to make an annual contribution to its running costs. It must have been with some trepidation that the BTO first asked its supporters if they would take part in the project and make a contribution to its costs. However, such was the generosity of the BTO supporters that, by the end of the first year of recording, 5,028 participants had become involved. Since that time, Garden BirdWatch has continued to grow and by September 2003, the project involved over 16,000 garden birdwatchers – a remarkable achievement.

Over the period during which Garden BirdWatch has been running, there has also been growth in the resources and level of technology used to manage the project. Initially, Garden BirdWatch was coordinated on a part time basis by Derek Toomer, assisted by Tracey Brookes, both of whom were also involved in other BTO work. Andrew Cannon took over the role of coordinating the project in 1996 and was soon joined by two part-time assistants, Jacky Prior and Carol Povey. Mike Toms took over from Andrew Cannon in 2001 and the team were joined by a third part-time assistant, Margaret Askew, in 2003. Many volunteers have also helped with the running of the project. Today, the BTO/CJ Garden BirdWatch project is the largest year-round citizen science project on garden birds anywhere in the World!

The Garden BirdWatch method

Garden BirdWatch gathers information in a way that makes it possible to measure relative change in the use that birds make of gardens. This approach is similar to that behind other long-running BTO projects and it is particularly suited to large-scale projects covering a wide range of species at many different recording sites.

The scanner by Mike Toms

The sheer size of Garden BirdWatch imposes constraints on the type of research questions that can be addressed and the way in which data may be collected. Fortunately, the type of information gathered can readily be coded on forms that can be automatically read by a scanning machine. This machine reads the forms simply by detecting the contrast between dark ink-filled boxes and the light background.

Garden BirdWatchers are asked to record birds using their gardens, making records from the same place (their defined 'recording area') at more or less the same time or times each week. Continuity of recording effort is more important than the quantity of recording. For the paper forms used by the bulk of participants, 42 common garden species are split into two groups: the ten most frequently seen garden birds from a previous pilot study (known as Table A species) and the remaining 32 (Table B species).

For the Table A species, participants record the size of the largest group of each species seen together in the garden at any one time during the course of the recording week. This use of the 'largest group' avoids double-counting and ensures consistency in defining the recording unit from one week to the next. For Table B species, only presence or absence is noted. All other species, those not included on the scannable form, are recorded on a separate sheet that is submitted once a year. The normal recording form covers a 13 week recording period and is submitted quarterly.

About a quarter of active Garden BirdWatchers submit their weekly observations over the Internet. Online participation enables individual Garden BirdWatchers to view all their own data, including those originally submitted on the paper forms. The observations are validated as they are entered and the information is then automatically loaded into the massive Garden BirdWatch database. Overnight, various programs run automatically to generate reporting rate graphs, summary tables and scrolling maps showing the location of recent sightings.

Alongside the information recorded on birds, other details are gathered on the site at which the recording takes place. These include information about the other features present within the garden recording area, as well as on the nature of surrounding habitats. This information has been used to examine which factors may determine the nature of the bird community visiting gardens at different times of the year.

Recording food provision

It is extremely important to gather weekly information on the foods provided at each site, since the provision of food has been shown to have a significant effect on the use of gardens by birds. The food provided can be factored in when seasonal or regional patterns of bird data are being analysed. This plot shows the proportion of gardens providing peanuts each week.

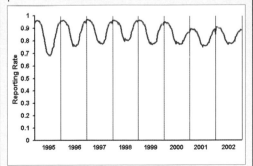

Peanuts by CJ WildBird Foods

Garden BirdWatch results

The vast Garden BirdWatch dataset can be analysed in many different ways. One of the simplest ways of showing how the use of gardens changes over time is by presenting reporting rate graphs (see boxes). The reporting rate is simply the number of gardens containing the species in a given week, divided by the total number of gardens at which recording was carried out during that week. For example, a reporting rate value of 0.5 would mean that the species was recorded in half (50%) of the gardens that week. More complex analyses can be performed using the count data gathered through Garden BirdWatch or by looking at differences that may exist between regions (see page 34), habitats or seasons. It is also possible to examine how the use of gardens changes in relation to temperature, snow cover and other weather-related variables.

In addition to providing information on the seasonal patterns of garden use, the Garden BirdWatch results can also give us important information on longer-term changes. Increases in Garden BirdWatch reporting rates for species like Goldfinch and Woodpigeon (see box) are the result of changes in populations of these species within other habitats. In the case of the Woodpigeon, a change in cropping practices within agricultural land appears to have

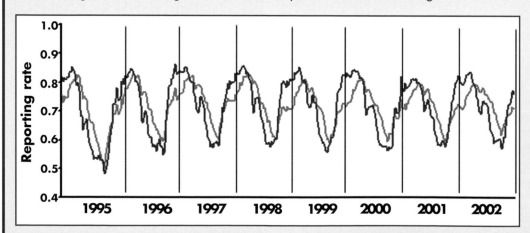

Similarities and differences

Although many species follow the general pattern of winter peak and late summer or autumn trough, there are often more subtle differences between individual species in their use of gardens. Greenfinches (green) and Chaffinches (blue) both move into gardens over the same few weeks during late autumn but, while the reporting rate for Chaffinch keeps going up, that for Greenfinch levels off before going up again in the New Year. Once the reporting rates for these two species
have peaked they begin to fall, as the breeding season approaches and birds leave gardens, either to breed in other habitats or to return to breeding grounds elsewhere in Europe. What is of particular interest is that the Chaffinches leave first, several weeks before the Greenfinches, even though the two arrived together. This may tie in with the timing of the breeding season. By monitoring these patterns over a long run of years Garden BirdWatch will be able to provide useful supplementary information on changes in the timing of the breeding season, which may relate to climate change.

Greenfinch by Tommy Holden

increased overwinter survival and has resulted in an increase in the Woodpigeon population, particularly in the south and east of England. The Goldfinch population in farmland has been recovering from an earlier population decline but the species has also begun to exploit the wider range of supplementary foods and feeding opportunities provided in gardens.

Greenfinches by Jill Pakenham

Several of the declining farmland seed-eaters are regularly reported from rural gardens during late winter. In the case of the Yellowhammer this decline is still continuing, something that can be seen from the Garden BirdWatch reporting rate for this species (see box). In this instance, the Garden BirdWatch trend is similar to that produced by other farmland surveys, reinforcing the message to conservation bodies that the species is in difficulty.

For other species, where much of the population breeds in urban and suburban areas, Garden BirdWatch provides one of the best tools for monitoring population change. The ongoing decline of House Sparrow and Starling populations in urban and suburban

Ups and downs

By running a project in a consistent manner over many years, it is possible to gather information on population change. Many such changes tend to be gradual in nature, with a small percentage increase or decrease each year, often masked by the short-term effects of weather events, such as a severe winter or a summer drought.

a) Goldfinch

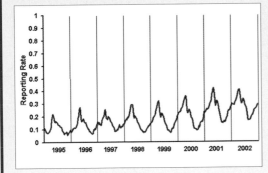

b) Woodpigeon

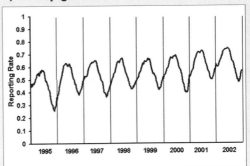

c) Yellowhammer

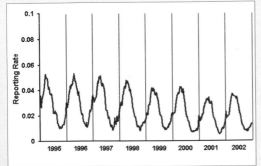

d) House Sparrow

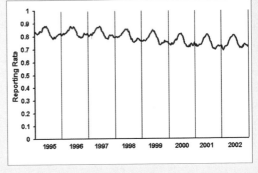

areas is revealed by both the Garden Bird Feeding Survey and Garden BirdWatch. However, it is only through Garden BirdWatch, with its large number of participants and good geographical coverage, that regional differences in the rates of decline can be determined.

For the House Sparrow, a significant decreasing population trend across the UK masks tremendous regional differences. The decline is most pronounced in the southeast, whilst populations in Wales and Scotland appear almost stable. The regional pattern for Starling (see box) is complicated by the presence of varying numbers of immigrant Starlings during the winter months. Careful examination of the plots suggests a decline in both our breeding and wintering populations in southeast England. This sort of information, presented regionally, can be used to establish the underlying causes behind population change.

One of the most valuable and exciting aspects of Garden BirdWatch is the range of uses to which the information gathered can be put. In addition to telling us how and why birds use gardens, Garden BirdWatch also provides an insight into what is happening to birds in other habitats and could make a very valuable contribution to the BTO's Integrated Population Monitoring Programme, which provides conservation agencies with information about species in difficulty. Garden BirdWatch would not have been able to fulfil this potential were it not for the generosity and commitment of the Garden BirdWatchers.

Regional patterns

Regional differences in Garden BirdWatch reporting rates can be used to help discover the reasons for the observed decline in Starling numbers noted by other surveys. The falling reporting rate for southeast England is very different from the pattern seen elsewhere in Britain and Ireland.

Southeast England
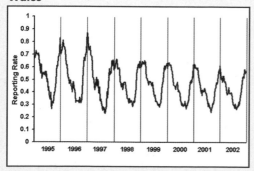

Southern Scotland
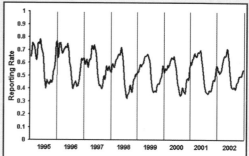

Wales
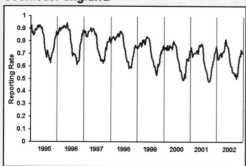

Ireland
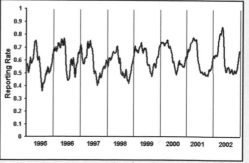

Starling by Tommy Holden

Garden bird ecology

Bird behaviour

The daily cycle

Annual patterns

Movement and migration

Life and death

Nuthatch
by Tommy Holden

There are some interesting differences between the behaviours exhibited by birds and those of other animals. For example, while birds display rapid learning ability, they generally do not exhibit the types of 'play' behaviour seen in mammals. Such differences are thought to result from the rapid development that is characteristic of birds. Small birds often attain their adult weight and size in just a few weeks, a duration that may equate to just 1% of their total life expectancy. In many mammals, especially primates, adult size and weight are not reached until 30% of total life expectancy has passed. Hence, the high development rates of birds may favour rapid learning but preclude play. By watching garden birds, it may be possible to witness a wide range of different behaviours, including those linked with territory acquisition, mate selection and the exploitation of novel foodstuffs.

Starlings by Tommy Holden

Flocks and communal roosting

Many garden bird species are seen in flocks, especially outside the breeding season. This is because being part of a flock may offer advantages to an individual bird, particularly increased vigilance. For species that feed out in the open, each individual balances the need to feed with the need to watch out for predators. With lots of individuals gathered together in a flock, there are always likely to be some individuals with their heads up looking for predators while other have their heads down feeding. The advantage of being an individual within a flock of similar individuals is that a predator faced with many targets often finds it difficult to single one out.

Some flocks may be made up of individuals of more than one species, for example the roving flocks of tits and warblers that are a feature of late autumn. Again, these offer increased levels of vigilance but have a further advantage in that the different species making up the flock are likely to feed on different things or in different ways, thus providing mutual security with minimal competition. It is known that tits specialise in feeding on different parts of a tree, with the smallest and most agile species concentrating their efforts at the ends of branches. This means that their mixed flocks effectively partition the available resources.

Some of the most familiar flocks are those formed by roosting Starlings. During the autumn, small flocks of Starlings roost close to the areas in which they are feeding but later in the year they tend to gather in much larger flocks that roost together at favoured sites, often used year after year. Small groups of Starlings will gather together at pre-roosting sites and birds from a wide area may form up into vast flocks that perform spectacular aerobatic displays immediately prior to dropping into the final roost site.

A single bird may lose 15% or more of its weight trying to keep warm on a cold winter night, and communal roosting may help birds to conserve energy by reducing heat loss. Roosts may also act as information centres, where individuals can learn about the best feeding opportunities. Individual birds appear able to assess the condition of their neighbours, judging which ones have had the most successful day's feeding. In the morning, individuals that had a poor day foraging the day before can follow those birds in good condition to feeding grounds where food is abundant. Flocks tend to form in those bird species that feed on food resources that are usually superabundant and patchily distributed. Those species for which food resources are less abundant or less spatially clumped, tend to set up feeding territories or to feed alone.

Song

Bird song is usually linked to the acquisition and defence of territory or for the attraction of a mate. Almost all song is generated by the male and appears to be under the control of the male sex hormone, testosterone. In a few species, both sexes may sing for all or part of the year. In the Robin, the female maintains her own territory outside of the breeding season and she will defend this against other females, using song to advertise her ownership of an area. During the breeding season, when paired with a male, female Robins tend to remain silent.

Wren by Tommy Folden

Most bird song is part of a clear seasonal cycle, linked to breeding and territory establishment. The amount of song produced sometimes declines after the birds pair up (*e.g.* Sedge Warbler) but in other species it may only decrease when the eggs are being laid or when the bird is undergoing its annual moult. Such differences in the pattern of song intensity can be used to discover the function behind bird song. For example, it is known that female birds may use the song of a male to determine his suitability as a mate. For Stonechats, research showed that males with higher rates of singing were better parents, helping to feed the chicks and defend the nest more than males with lower singing rates. Song has also been shown to have a role in establishing and maintaining territorial boundaries. A clever experiment by Charles Krebs neatly demonstrated the role of song in territorial defence. Krebs temporarily removed territory-holding male Great Tits and replaced some of them with an elaborate system of loudspeakers, playing their songs. In territories where the loudspeakers were used, no other Great Tits set up new territories. In those where no speakers were placed, new males quickly established territories of their own.

Feather maintenance

It is essential for a bird to keep its feathers in good condition, both for the purposes of flight and insulation. Routine maintenance involves a number of different behaviours, many of which may be seen in garden birds.

Many birds bathe using water, either splashing themselves in a suitable pool or bird bath or by dew-bathing against wet vegetation. In most cases, the bird attempts to moisten the surface of its feathers rather than actually soak them. This helps the preen oil to spread across the feathers. Other birds, *e.g.* House Sparrows, dust bathe, another behaviour geared towards feather maintenance. Preening typically follows bathing and, in many species, this involves working the preen oil across the feathers. This oil is produced from a preen gland that is located just above the tail.

Preening is used to manipulate the feathers, realigning the individual filaments that hook together to give each feather its shape. Birds can sometimes be seen 'nibbling' their flight feathers, carefully working each one in turn.

Blue Tit by Dick Jeeves

The daily cycle

It is apparent from watching birds at garden feeding stations that some species arrive at feeders very early in the morning, while others put in an appearance much later in the day. Such differences between species have a biological basis and are linked to ecology, behaviour and physiology. There is also a strong seasonality to the time of day when particular species may be seen. For example, during the breeding season, adult birds have to forage for longer in order to find sufficient food to support both themselves and their growing chicks. During winter, birds may show a different daily cycle, driven by their need to take on the energy reserves required to get them through the long winter nights.

General patterns

Throughout much of the year, there appears to be a general pattern to when individual species make use of garden feeding stations. Blackbirds are usually the first birds to be noted, their chattering alarm calls piercing the pre-dawn gloom and, as any bird ringer will tell you, Blackbirds are often the first birds to be caught at an early morning ringing session within a garden setting. Robins are also active early on and both of these species

have large eyes, relative to their body size. They can also be heard singing at night, spurred on by street lighting. In fact, many reports of Nightingales turn out to be Robins or Blackbirds because people wrongly assume that only the Nightingale delivers its song at night. Soon after the arrival of the Blackbirds and Robins, just as it is getting light, the various tit species appear at feeders (see box) and these often have hanging feeders to themselves for some time, before the late-rising Greenfinches and House Sparrows put in an appearance.

The daily cycle in winter

In general, most species show three peaks to their levels of feeding activity during a typical winter day. The first of these occurs during the early morning and is thought to be an attempt by individual birds, emerging from their roosts, to top up energy reserves lost the previous night. A later peak, occurring towards the end of the day, probably has a similar cause, with birds taking on extra reserves to help them get through the night ahead. The absence of birds in late morning and early afternoon suggests that small birds are balancing the risk of predation against the benefits gained from energy-rich foods.

When to feed

Research carried out by Susan Fitzpatrick, looking at temporal patterns of feeder use by birds in a Belfast garden, has highlighted interesting differences in the arrival patterns of various tit species at hanging feeders during the winter. As well as differences resulting from weather conditions, daylight length and temperature, Fitzpatrick found that the various species (and sexes) arrived according to a hierarchy of body size. Female Coal Tits and Blue Tits arrived first, followed by the males and later followed by female and male Great Tits. The existence of such a hierarchy results from the differing energetics of these small birds. The smallest individuals and species store less fat for use overnight than larger birds and also have a higher metabolic rate, due to greater loss of

heat. This means that these are the individuals that need to begin feeding earlier in the morning, in order to make up the shortfall. The same observation could be explained by competition, in that larger birds, like Great Tits, House Sparrows and Greenfinches, tend to dominate feeding stations, so smaller and less dominant species may be forced to feed at times when larger species are not using the feeders.

Blue Tit by Tommy Holden

There is a third peak, smaller in size, which occurs during the middle of the day. This peak does not fit with the predictions made by these predation-risk models but may be a consequence of competition between species for access to limited food resources. The smaller, subordinate, species may be forced to visit feeders at a time which is not ideal (according to the risk of predation) because larger species exclude them from the feeders at the better times of day.

One other complicating factor in all this is the predictability of the food supply. Most garden feeding stations represent a predictable food supply, so birds can rely on being able to top up their fat reserves late in the day in readiness for the night ahead. This means that they do not have to feed continuously and hence carry around extra fat reserves all day, which may make them less manoeuvrable and more readily caught by a predator. Research has shown that, where food supplies are less predictable, small birds will increase their energy reserves at the earliest opportunity, presumably because the risk of starvation will be higher than the risk of being predated.

Daily cycle in the breeding season

Although the daily pattern of activity in garden birds during the summer is still influenced by food availability, it is also under the influence of breeding biology. Breeding birds have a wider range of needs to balance at this time of year and the daily routine varies, depending upon the stage of the breeding cycle and its associated behaviours. One of the most interesting aspects of the daily cycle during the breeding season is the timing of egg-laying. Small garden birds typically produce one egg each day during the period of egg-laying. In most species the egg is laid around sunrise but in the Woodpigeon laying takes place early in the afternoon and in the Pheasant it takes place in the evening. Female Blue Tits roost in the nest cavity overnight and usually lay an egg at first light before leaving the nest. However, on occasion, the female may leave the nest and return a little later to deposit the egg. In a species like the Blue Tit, where the eggs all hatch at the same time, the egg will then be covered with nesting material and incubation will not begin until the clutch has been completed. In other species, incubation may begin with the first egg, or part way through the laying period.

The dawn chorus

The dawn chorus is perhaps the most characteristic and recognisable component of the daily cycle during the early part of the breeding season. This chorus of bird song, from many different species, usually begins before dawn and lasts for some time before ending, often abruptly. Song is used to define and defend territories and many researchers consider the dawn chorus to represent the trade-off between the competing needs to defend a territory and to find food, with fitter birds able to sing for longer. Various explanations have been put forward to explain its timing so early in the morning. The dawn chorus occurs at a time when territorial intrusions have been shown to be at their peak and it is also the time when low light intensity may limit feeding opportunities and reduce the effectiveness of visual displays of territory ownership.

Robin by George Higginbotham

Garden birdwatchers are well aware of the comings and goings within their gardens, as different species make use of the habitat and resources available at partiular times of the year. However, it is only through the BTO/CJ Garden BirdWatch project that we have been able to quantify such patterns and to establish their biological basis. Previous studies of garden birds had tended to concentrate on individual species at single sites, often for only part of the year, but Garden BirdWatch gathers information from many thousands of gardens, spread right across the country, throughout the year.

Yellowhammer by Tommy Holden

General patterns

Seasonality to the use of gardens is obvious in some species, notably those which are summer migrants or winter visitors, but it can also be seen in species like Blue Tit and Blackbird (see box) that many would regard as being resident throughout the year. Seasonal patterns to the use of gardens are shown in the species accounts through a seasonality graph based on Garden BirdWatch observations. There are a number of general patterns that can be seen. Among the resident species (*e.g.* Blackbird, Blue Tit and Robin) there is a distinct autumn trough to the Garden BirdWatch reporting rate, consistent from one year to the next in its timing and magnitude. This occurs during the period when natural food is widely available outside gardens, either within the wider countryside or in areas of rough ground within urban landscapes (*e.g.* railway embankments or brown-field sites) . With foods such as blackberries and thistle seeds

available, birds become less reliant on the supplementary food put out in gardens and their absence often prompts calls from concerned birdwatchers whose gardens appear devoid of birds. It is also a time of year when many bird species undergo a moult of their feathers. During the moult, most species become shy and retiring, as they attempt to avoid the unwanted attentions of predators while their flight capabilities are diminished.

Summer migrants and winter visitors show a pronounced seasonality to their use of gardens, which often matches the period during which they are present within Britain and Ireland. The pattern shown by summer migrants is likely to be more consistent from year to year than that of the winter visitors, since the timing of arrival of many of the winter visitors is determined by food shortages and weather elsewhere. One of the best examples of the magnitude of variation in the peak reporting rate between years can be seen in the Brambling. This species winters in Britain and Ireland in varying numbers, depending largely upon the availability of beech mast. In years with a poor crop of beech mast the Garden BirdWatch reporting rate is high but in years with a good crop it is much reduced. The timing of arrival of winter visitors can also be dependent upon weather conditions. Cold-weather influxes of Starlings from continental Europe, both new arrivals and of birds from the countryside, appear as peaks to the Garden BirdWatch reporting rate during the winter months.

Other species normally resident within other habitats in Britain and Ireland may also show a seasonal pattern to their use of gardens. In a species such as the Reed Bunting, the Garden BirdWatch reporting rate is low throughout the year but shows a peak during late spring. This peak is most pronounced in rural gardens, suggesting that food provided at garden feeding stations may be important when seed availability in farmland is lowest. A number of species show increased use of gardens at other times of year, again coinciding with periods when favoured food resources are unavailable. The Garden BirdWatch reporting rate for Jackdaw has a peak in early summer, a time of year when the adults find it particularly difficult to find sufficient food for their chicks, while that for Great Spotted Woodpecker also shows an early summer peak, this time when adults bring their young to peanut feeders.

The Garden BirdWatch reporting rate peaks for some species differ according to garden type and that for Blackcap is perhaps the most interesting of these. Although Blackcaps are mainly summer migrants, they have started to winter in Britain and Ireland as well (see pages 80–81). In urban and suburban gardens, the reporting rates peak in winter and are quite a bit higher than those for rural gardens. However, in the summer, the reporting rate in urban and suburban gardens is much lower and, what's more, it is lower than that for rural gardens. Wintering Blackcaps appear to favour urban and suburban gardens, while the summer populations appear to favour rural gardens. This must reflect their requirements of insect food and nest sites in dense scrub during the summer and the availability of suitable foods and warmer conditions at urban and suburban sites during the winter.

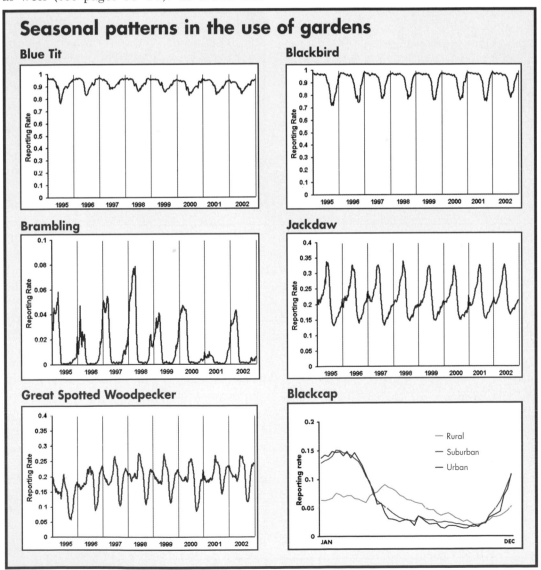

Seasonal patterns in the use of gardens

Blue Tit

Blackbird

Brambling

Jackdaw

Great Spotted Woodpecker

Blackcap

Birds have a remarkable ability to cover long distances and to cross areas of unsuitable habitat in search of more favourable conditions elsewhere. The ability to fly frees them from many of the constraints faced by other groups of animals that may limit their populations and movements. The movements made by birds fall into a number of categories and, although individual movements may sometimes serve more than one purpose, it is worth looking at them as distinct processes.

Migration is the most extreme form of movement made by birds, taking them on a predictable and (largely) annual flight between two distinct areas, one used for breeding and the other used for wintering. Such migrations result from the fact that most bird food resources, notably insects, are strongly seasonal. Most of our summer migrants are insectivores and breed in Britain and Ireland during the long daylight hours that our northern summers provide. Towards winter, the insect abundance falls and the insect eaters are forced to retreat south to latitudes where insects remain readily available.

Other migrants visiting Britain and Ireland arrive for the winter, notably those species avoiding colder conditions further north and east (see box). Many of these summer and winter migrants are obvious visitors since they are only here for part of the year. However, there are other populations that also migrate to Britain and Ireland but which go unnoticed (*e.g.* Blackbird, Greenfinch and Chaffinch) because they mingle with our own resident breeding populations. Migration is not always an "all or nothing" process and some populations or species undergo a partial migration, where some individuals may migrate while others do not. Usually these partial migrants are responding to weather conditions or food availability, which explains why such movements may not happen every year.

Migration is a complex process, not least because each migrating bird will need to navigate from its breeding ground to where it is going to spend the winter. The bird has to know where it is going and how it is going to get there. In the case of young birds this will be to a place it has not been before. Birds have been shown to use a range of different mechanisms to help them navigate: some use a star compass, some a sun compass, others use the Earth's magnetic field or a combination of methods. As well as a requirement to follow a route, the individual bird has to allow for the effect of weather conditions and be able to reorientate itself if blown off course.

Juvenile Swallow by Tommy Holden

Some birds are able to feed as they migrate (*e.g.* Swallows and Swifts) but others either have to carry sufficient reserves of fat to make the entire journey or stop *en route* at sites where they can feed and refuel. The amount of fuel reserves that a bird takes on is not only influenced by what it can carry but must be balanced against other costs, like increased risk of predation or slower flight speed. Many small birds fatten up before they begin their migration, sometimes feeding on different foods from those they would normally take. All of these processes interact to form the complex series of behaviours that make up migration. This is why migration takes so many different forms, from the long-distance annual migration across the equator made by Swallows, to the short-distance movements made by Pied Wagtails breeding in northern Britain. The subject of migration is a book in itself.

Irruptions and eruptions

For some species, the availability of favoured foods may not simply change with season but may also vary (often dramatically) from one year to the next. This is particularly true for those species that feed upon berries (*e.g.* Fieldfare and Waxwing), tree seeds (*e.g.* Brambling) or small mammals (birds of prey and owls). Under certain conditions, trees or shrubs may, over large areas, produce very few seeds or berries in a given year. This forces those birds that would normally feed on these seeds and fruits to move into other areas in search of food. These movements, known as eruptions (where the birds leave an area) and irruptions (where the birds arrive at an area), can result in the periodic arrival in gardens across Britain and Ireland of Waxwings, Fieldfares, Siskins and Bramblings in very large numbers.

Dispersal

During the first few months after fledging, young birds often move away from where they were born. This is known as 'dispersal' and for many species is part of the process of territory establishment. By moving away from where they were born, young birds lessen the chances of competing with their parents for limited resources like nest sites or food. In addition, such movements reduce the level of inbreeding, something that is further accomplished by the fact that young females typically disperse a greater distance than young males. Although these dispersal distances may be many kilometres, in most species they are much shorter. For example, the average natal dispersal distance for Great Tits is only four to seven territory widths – not much at all.

We know about bird movements thanks to the efforts of bird ringers (see box on page 46) but the occurrence of such movements can also be seen in data gathered by projects like the BTO Migration Watch (see page 63) or by Garden BirdWatch itself. The seasonal pattern to many of the reporting rates reflects the movements into and out of gardens by a wide range of bird species. Cold weather movements of Starlings into gardens are an obvious example, as are the late winter reporting rate peaks of Yellowhammers and Tree Sparrows.

Origins of winter visitors

Blackbird

Redwing

Chaffinch

Brambling

Fieldfare

Starling

Illustrations by Simon Gillings

Life and death

Garden birds face many hazards during the course of their short lives, so it is not that surprising to discover just how high their mortality rates actually are. Individuals have to face predators, find sufficient food, avoid disease and contend with a range of man-made hazards.

Longevity

One of the most commonly asked questions is 'How long do birds live?' This is not usually a straightforward question to answer because scientists studying bird populations tend to think in terms of survival rather than longevity. Although there is published information from bird ringing on the maximum recorded times between ringing and death (or recapture) of different species of wild birds (see box), the information from bird ringing is usually used to calculate annual survival rates. These can best be explained by considering a population of 100 birds, of the same species, all born in the same year. It might be that just 20 of these 100 birds survive their first winter, which gives an annual survival rate of 20%. Ten of these

20 birds might then survive through to the next year, giving an annual survival rate of 50% for this second year. Note that the survival rate has increased – because inexperienced, young birds tend to have lower survival rates than adults. The annual survival rate for the next year may remain at 50%, leaving only five of our original 100 birds alive. If this continues, then the number of survivors will drop to two or three the following year and all the individuals will have died within another couple of years.

In most studies, survival rates are calculated on an annual basis but they can be calculated over other time periods or for a particular phase of the bird's life. This approach means that differences in survival rates between males and females, or between birds of different ages, can be examined and used to understand ecology and population trends. The methods used in survival rate analyses have now developed to a stage where complex models can be fitted using specially written computer programs. Such programs are regularly used by BTO scientists to find out why certain species are in decline.

How long can birds live?

Species	Longevity record (years:months:days)	Species	Longevity record (years:months:days)
Grey Heron	21:05:16	Blackcap	10:08:15
Sparrowhawk	17:01:11	Goldcrest	04:10:09
Black-headed Gull	26:03:08	Blue Tit	09:09:03
Collared Dove	16:11:02	Great Tit	13:11:05
Swallow	11:01:11	Nuthatch	11:09:10
Wren	06:08:13	Jackdaw	15:11:16
Dunnock	11:03:07	Starling	16:03:04
Robin	08:04:30	House Sparrow	12:00:12
Blackbird	14:02:01	Chaffinch	11:07:21
Song Thrush	10:08:29	Greenfinch	12:00:15

One of the main problems with using ringing information to calculate longevity records is that those species for which a large number of individuals have been ringed, and subsequently found dead, are more likely to include a particularly old individual than for a species with only a few recoveries. Most individuals do not live anywhere near as long as these longevity records suggest.

Causes of mortality

Although garden birds gain a number of benefits from living within gardens, there are disadvantages and hazards that individual birds may face, which are more significant than in other habitats. It is possible to get some idea of the relative importance of these different hazards from bird ringing, by looking at the reported circumstances under which birds have been found dead within gardens. However, these need to be treated with care, since some finding circumstances (*e.g.* being killed by a cat or flying into a window) may be more obvious than others (*e.g.* dying from disease or old age). It is also possible to look at the effect of different factors on nesting success, by using information gathered through the BTO's Nest Record Scheme.

Sparrowhawks by Mike Toms

Predators

The most significant predator of garden birds is the domestic cat and a number of studies have already quantified the impact that these predators can have on wildlife. One study, conducted in the Bedfordshire village of Felmersham, revealed that at least one-third of all House Sparrow deaths in the village were due to cat predation. Although this is a staggering figure, it should be stressed that we do not know what effect this level of mortality would have had on the House Sparrow population. If food availability were the main factor controlling overwinter survival and population size in the sparrow population, then the high level of mortality attributable to cat predation may simply have reduced competition for food and enabled more sparrows to survive the winter. Under

such circumstances the cat predation may not have had any impact on the size of the House Sparrow population. However, more research into this is urgently required, allowing the effects of cat predation to be quantified at the population level. Once this has been done, and if cat predation is shown to be a problem, then it is up to government to determine if legislation is required. In some countries, the ownership of a cat requires a licence and both the number of cats and their access to the outside are controlled. Research has shown that the amount of predation varies between individual cats and that older cats catch fewer prey items than younger ones.

Sparrowhawks also predate garden birds and appear where small birds are abundant. Unlike the domestic cat, the Sparrowhawk is a native predator and part of a natural system, its population effectively controlled by the availability of food. Despite detailed studies having been carried out to investigate the link between Sparrowhawk predation and the decline of certain songbird species, there is no evidence to support the argument, put forward by some, that Sparrowhawks have caused songbird populations to decline. In fact, there is strong evidence supporting the opposite view, that neither Sparrowhawks nor Magpies are to blame.

There are a number of species that may predate the nests of garden birds, including Magpie, Jay, Carrion Crow, Great Spotted Woodpecker, grey squirrel and various small mammals. While the corvid species will take the eggs and young of open nesting species, woodpeckers, squirrels, mice and weasels can also gain access to small birds using nestboxes. Each of these predators may wreck a nesting attempt, or all nesting attempts within a local area, but their national impact is unlikely to be significant. Remember, while a Blackbird may lose its first nest, it normally has the opportunity to try two or even three more times during the course of the breeding season, and only one or two of the resulting chicks need to reach breeding age in order for the population to remain stable.

Man-made hazards

The two most important man-made hazards facing garden birds appear to be motor-traffic and windows. Substantial numbers of birds are killed by cars and, although this is not just a problem in built-up areas, this can account for much of the mortality that occurs in this habitat.

Many birds are killed by flying into windows. In some instances a bird can see through a pair of windows and assume that it can fly through to reach the other side. In other cases, the bird flies into the window after it sees the sky or trees reflected in the glass. Such misjudgements can occur when a bird is panicked into making a quick response to a perceived threat, either the sighting of a predator or an approaching human. Currently, we do not know how this form of mortality may impact upon the populations of different garden bird species but we do know that the Red-listed Song Thrush is a species which seems especially prone to window-strikes. This is an area of research to which Garden BirdWatchers could make an important contribution.

A bird stunned as a result of flying into a window should be placed in a cardboard box and left in a dark, quiet, warm place for a couple of hours. With luck, the bird will have recovered and can be released in the garden. If the bird has not recovered then it may be necessary to seek veterinary advice. Special window stickers, known as sentinels, can be placed on windows to help lessen the chances of birds flying into them.

There are other hazards that birds may encounter when living within garden habitats. These include becoming entangled in netting, getting shut in buildings and coming into contact with noxious chemicals. One further problem can occur when hedges are cut or reroofing work is carried out during the breeding season. This may result in the nesting birds deserting their eggs or young.

The Ringing Scheme and reporting a ringed bird

Every year, in Britain and Ireland, about 750,000 birds are fitted with uniquely numbered rings. Different designs are used for different species, to ensure that they are a perfect fit and do not inconvenience the bird. On average, fewer than one in fifty of these ringed birds is subsequently reported to the BTO. This 'reporting rate' is higher for large obvious species (e.g. Mute Swan) than it is for small migrant species like Swallow and  Chiffchaff. Bird ringers use a variety of methods to catch birds for ringing. Most individuals are caught in fine nets erected between two poles but about a fifth of the birds ringed each year are ringed as chicks at the nest.

Ringing not only provides important information on the movements made by birds, it also enables scientists to calculate survival rates (see page 44), which are used to find out why populations may be in decline. The success of the Ringing Scheme relies on 2,000 trained, volunteer ringers and those people kind enough to send in any rings that they find. It is always worth checking any dead bird to see if it is fitted with a ring. If you find one, please write down the ring number and, if the bird is dead, please enclose the flattened ring taped to your letter. Include details of where the bird was found, including the name of the nearest town and (if possible) a grid reference, as well as the date, information on the circumstances surrounding the bird being found (e.g. hit by a car, brought in by your cat) and your own name and address, so that information about where the bird was ringed can be sent to you. Details can be reported to the BTO by post, phone or via www.bto.org, or to the Natural History Museum address given on the ring.

Flattened rings by Mark Collier

Species accounts

Sparrowhawk

With its slender body, short broad wings and long tail, the Sparrowhawk is ideally adapted to hunting within woodland. Its long legs and extended central toes are characteristic of a bird of prey specialising on catching other birds, making this a highly efficient hunter. Because of this, the Sparrowhawk is sometimes regarded as a villain, the perceived reason for the widespread decline of many songbirds. However, all the scientific evidence so far gathered strongly suggests that the Sparrowhawk is not the reason behind these declines. Certainly, there was no great upsurge in songbird populations when Sparrowhawks declined and there has been no sudden decline of favoured prey species, such as Greenfinch, Great Tit and Collared Dove, now their numbers have recovered.

The Sparrowhawk is now one of the most abundant and widely distributed raptor species in Britain and Ireland but just a few decades ago it was all but extinct in many eastern counties, following the introduction of organochlorine pesticides for use in agriculture. These are fat-soluble and incredibly persistent, readily accumulating in the bodies of top predators like the Sparrowhawk. While compounds like aldrin and dieldrin brought about the direct mortality of adults, others, notably DDT, reduced the thickness of Sparrowhawk eggshells and led to increased breakages during incubation. This resulted in a massive drop in the breeding population, which only began to recover once these chemicals had been phased out. Even today, the legacy of DDT is still detectable in Sparrowhawk eggs. The current Sparrowhawk population is probably larger than it was before the decline, partly because of reduced levels of persecution but also a consequence of the establishment of conifer plantations in upland areas which they now occupy. Recent decades have also seen a spread into many suburban and urban gardens and parks, with Sparrowhawks exploiting the abundance of small birds using garden feeding stations.

Sparrowhawks rely on woodland for nesting and established pairs tend to build new nests close to those used in previous years. Male Sparrowhawks typically hunt within woodland (see box) while females are the ones to venture farther afield into more open countryside. Although some pairs will build a nest in a smaller stand of trees within parkland or a shelter-belt, a typical nest site will be in a conifer in fairly thick woodland. Egg-laying seems to begin some weeks after the nest has been built and research has shown that it usually starts about 5–10 days after the first fledgling songbirds appear in the Sparrowhawk diet. This dependence upon the presence of fledgling songbirds to initiate breeding highlights the close dependence of this predator on its prey. Food shortage is the commonest cause of Sparrowhawk nest desertion in Britain.

Sparrowhawk by Dick Jeeves

During incubation, and while the chicks are still young, the female remains on the nest, supported by the male who brings food for her and the developing chicks. Once the young are larger, both parents will bring food back to the nest, the female only tending to brood the chicks when the weather is poor. The young grow quickly and leave the nest after about four weeks, although they are supported for another three to four weeks by their parents, once they have left. There is then a period of dispersal, as the chicks search for territories of their own.

Female Sparrowhawk by Derek Belsey

Sparrowhawks use the available cover to get as close to their prey as possible before making a rapid attack. Sometimes they will hunt from a perch while at other times they will hunt in flight, following the contours of the land to get as close as possible to an intended target. This is why you will often see a Sparrowhawk working along a hedgerow, swapping from side to side, or coming in through a garden from behind available cover. A very wide range of bird species is taken as prey but it is those species that feed out in the open or which are conspicuous that are the most often taken. Cryptic, cover-loving species or those with rapid flight only feature occasionally in the diet.

Big is beautiful

A female Sparrowhawk is about twice the size of her mate. While a typical male will weigh about 140g, an average female will weigh some 260g. Although it is not uncommon for female raptors to be larger than males, the Sparrowhawk shows the largest such difference in any bird of prey. The size difference of the two sexes allows each to employ a different role. The smaller male is an agile and efficient hunter, well suited to the task of provisioning the female while she incubates the eggs. The larger females carry the extra body reserves needed for reproduction and can survive for a number of days without food but they are less agile hunters. The males lack these reserves and live life on the limit – they need to catch food to survive – and this may be one of the reasons that males do not live as long as females. The difference in size also means that the two sexes focus on differently sized prey. Males take smaller birds like finches and tits, only occasionally catching birds as big as a Blackbird. Females tend to take Starlings and larger birds up to the size of an adult Woodpigeon.

Male Sparrowhawk by Tommy Holden

Status
Green listed. Population recovering and increasing.

Foods
Small birds up to the size of a Woodpigeon.

Breeding
Clutch size: 5–6
Incubates: 32–36 days
Young in nest: 24–30 days
No. broods: 1
Season: Apr–Aug

Seasonality

Jan　　　Dec

Pheasant

Status

Green listed.

Foods

Seeds, berries, plant material and insects.

Breeding

Clutch size: 8–15
Incubates: 22–27 days
Young in nest: n/a
No. broods: 1
Season: Mar–Aug

Seasonality

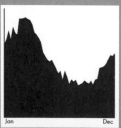

Jan   Dec

The Pheasant is the commonest gamebird in Britain and the most likely one to be encountered within a garden environment, especially in late winter. The greatest abundance of Pheasants tends to be on and around large shooting estates, where management often involves the hand-rearing and release of thousands of birds annually. It has been estimated that up to 25 million Pheasants may be released for shooting each year, a figure that dwarfs the 'wild' population. The Pheasant was probably originally introduced by the Normans and was certainly present in most of England and Scotland by the late 16th Century. In Wales, the species only really established itself fully during the latter part of the 19th Century, while in Ireland it remains relatively uncommon and probably survives only through reinforcement. Over the years, a number of different forms have been introduced to Britain in the hope that they might make better sporting birds. These forms have interbred with each other and so there is quite a bit of variation in the plumage of the familiar ring-necked males.

Pheasants are conspicuous birds and small groups may visit garden feeding stations to take seeds and grain at any time of the year. These foods, together with berries, plant tubers and weed seeds, are particularly important during the winter months. With the arrival of spring, Pheasants begin to increase the amount of animal food in their diet. Most of the winter groups are of only one sex. Females gather in larger groups (typically 2–4 birds but up to 20) than males (1–2 birds) and there is a clear hierarchy to group structure. From February, the males begin to establish their breeding territories, increasingly displaying to females and directing aggression towards other males. The males give a display combining a throaty call with wing-drumming, often from a prominent position. A successful male holding a good territory may attract a number of females, each of which will pair with him, while a male on a poor quality territory may fail to attract a mate at all.

Although Pheasants may be seen feeding on bird tables, they prefer to feed on the ground, scratching or digging for food. Pheasants may sometimes jump to reach berries hanging just out of reach and they have been reported to do the same thing to knock seed from hanging bird feeders.

Pheasants were originally birds of dense forest, so the bright colours of the males are somewhat conspicuous when seen in our countryside. One of the silliest sights is when a male crouches to hide in your vegetable patch, assuming that you can no longer see him! The drab females are much more cryptic, as one might expect of birds that spend three weeks incubating their eggs.

Male Pheasant by Tommy Holden

The Black-headed Gull is the most frequently reported gull species to visit garden feeding stations. The species has seen a remarkable change of fortune over the last two hundred years, recovering from near extinction in Britain during the 19th Century, with dramatic population increases during the 20th Century. These increases were accompanied by a rise in the use of inland areas for breeding, roosting and feeding, to the extent that birds started to visit bird tables in large urban areas like London. Black-headed Gulls most frequently appear in gardens during the cold winter months of January and February but are increasingly visiting gardens throughout the year, with dispersing birds often present during June and July. Outside of the winter, these garden visitors are usually immature, non-breeding birds from local colonies, recognisable by their brown wing feathers.

Being scavengers, Black-headed Gulls will take a very wide range of kitchen scraps, from meat and bread to cheese and potatoes. When feeding, they tend to be very aggressive and groups often squabble over the available food. Sometimes, particularly where food is presented in a relatively confined space, the birds don't land but instead dive down to snatch larger food items. Individuals appear bolder in cold weather. During the evening, birds gather to roost on areas of open water. Inland, these tend to be reservoirs, lakes and flooded gravel workings, while on the coast, they often roost on estuaries.

During the winter, our largely resident breeding population is joined by large numbers of immigrants from breeding populations scattered around the Baltic, the Low Countries and from as far east as Russia. It has been estimated that more than two-thirds of the birds wintering here may be immigrants, arriving over a protracted period from July to February. The earliest to arrive are usually young birds from breeding colonies in the Low Countries, while the last to arrive may be those forced by freezing weather to leave wintering grounds farther east. Once here, most of the winter visitors appear to be quite site faithful, even to the extent of returning to the same wintering sites in subsequent years. Despite the name, Black-headed Gulls don't have a black head. During the breeding season it is a dark chocolate brown colour, while in the winter the head is white, with a dark brown smudge on the side.

Summary

Summer

Winter

Status

Amber listed, decreasing in gardens.

Foods

Invertebrates, plant material, food scraps.

Breeding

Clutch size: 2–3
Incubates: 22–24 days
Young in nest: c.38 days
No. broods: 1
Season: Apr–Aug

Seasonality

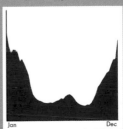

Jan   Dec

Adult, summer

First-year, winter

Black-headed Gulls by Derek Belsey & Mike Weston

Feral Pigeon

Winter

Status
Stable in gardens.

Foods
Plant material, seeds, invertebrates and scraps.

Breeding
Clutch size: 2
Incubates: 17–19 days
Young in nest: 27–30 days
No. broods: 3–5
Season: Jan–Dec

Seasonality

Jan   Dec

The familiar Feral Pigeon is descended from the Rock Dove, a species that has been domesticated for many thousands of years. Within Britain and Ireland, truly wild Rock Doves are now confined to remote sea-cliffs in the extreme north and west. Many of the Feral Pigeons breeding in urban areas have plumage which closely resembles that of their truly wild relatives, although there is a great variety of plumage forms, thanks mainly to the continued escape of birds from dovecotes and the thousands of racing pigeons that go astray each year. Intriguingly, melanistic birds appear to have more broods during the course of a year (sometimes five or six) than birds with 'wild type' plumage This may explain why dark morphs often dominate populations living within towns and cities.

Urban populations of Feral Pigeons have the capacity to increase rapidly, a consequence of their breeding ecology (young can breed at seven months of age), coupled with the favourable conditions in our unhygienic urban centres. Much money is spent to try to control Feral Pigeon numbers and thereby to remove the risk of disease transmission and reduce damage to buildings from the birds' droppings. Restricting access to favoured perches or nest sites may solve the problem at the local level but it simply forces birds to move elsewhere. Culling is largely ineffective because there is a large proportion of non-breeding birds to take over vacated nest sites. The only workable solution seems to be to remove their food supply, by changing peoples' attitudes towards the feeding of pigeons and the disposal of food waste.

Feral Pigeons can become a nuisance in gardens where kitchen scraps, bread or cheap bird food (full of wheat or other cereal grains) are provided. Since Feral Pigeons prefer to feed on the ground, the attractiveness of a garden feeding station can be reduced by only providing good quality feed (*e.g.* black sunflower seed) in hanging feeders. Ground feeding can continue if you can exclude the pigeons from the feeding area by surrounding it with a two-inch gauge wire mesh. The Garden BirdWatch reporting rate for this species averages about 10%, peaking in spring when food may be less abundant elsewhere. There has been a slight but steady increase in the Garden BirdWatch reporting since the project began in 1995.

Varying degrees of albinism and melanism occur within Feral Pigeon populations and a wide range of plumage patterns can be seen. Many individuals show signs of injury or disease, the latter often resulting from the crowded conditions under which they live.

Feral Pigeon by John Tully

For some garden birdwatchers, the Woodpigeon is an unwelcome visitor. It is easy to understand why, since one Woodpigeon can eat as much food as seven sparrows. The Woodpigeon boasts the dubious reputation of being the most economically damaging bird species in Britain and Ireland. Its pest status has increased as it has adapted to new agricultural crops, like oil seed rape, which provide Woodpigeons with a ready supply of green foodstuffs during the difficult winter months. Set against such problems with its image, the Woodpigeon remains one of the most biologically interesting of our garden birds. For example, the Woodpigeon is one of a very small number of birds that produce 'crop milk', a substance that is very similar to mammalian milk in its composition. The milk is produced, as the name suggests, in the crop, which is a sac-like structure normally used for storing food. During the last few days of the incubation period some of the cells lining the crop begin to produce milk, which forms the only source of nourishment during the first few days of young birds' lives. Other nestlings of seed-eating species have to be fed on animal material during their period of maximum growth.

Within urban areas, Woodpigeons usually nest in trees or tall shrubs but they have also been recorded nesting on ledges on buildings. The Garden BirdWatch reporting rate shows annually increasing use of gardens throughout the year. Woodpigeons were first noticed colonising urban areas some 180 years ago and they can often be seen feeding alongside Feral Pigeons. Many of these urban Woodpigeons feed on cheap seed mixes and on kitchen scraps, notably bread, and this may allow them to begin breeding earlier in the year than their rural cousins.

Woodpigeons can be gregarious in nature outside the breeding season but during spring the males set up small breeding territories. Ownership of these is advertised through the display flight – the male soaring upwards before stalling and executing one or two wing claps. The nest is a rather flimsy lattice of sticks, placed on a branch or in the fork of a tree or shrub. The breeding season is very long, with eggs having been found in every month of the year, although the main period of activity is over by the end of September.

Summer

Winter

Status

Green listed, increasing in gardens.

Foods

Plant material, seeds, ivy berries and grain.

Breeding

Clutch size: 2
Incubates: 16–17 days
Young in nest: 27 days
No. broods: 2 (3)
Season: Mar–Oct

Seasonality

An adult Woodpigeon is a large, plump bird with a white neck patch. There is a smudge of petrol-green above this. A young bird also has the patch of green but lacks the white of the adult. The 'coo-coo-coo-co-co' song, often heard during April and May, is a familiar part of the dawn chorus to most garden birdwatchers, and can be annoying if the bird happens to be calling from your chimney.

Woodpigeon by Mike Weston

Collared Dove

It is amazing to think that the now ubiquitous Collared Dove was first recorded breeding in Britain during the mid-1950s. This colonisation of Britain and Ireland was part of a larger range expansion which took place across Europe. Up until about 1930, Collared Doves were pretty much restricted, within Europe, to Turkey and parts of the Balkans. For some reason, possibly linked to a genetic change in the dispersal behaviour of young birds, the population began to push northwest across Europe. Over a period of something like 20 years, Collared Doves spread rapidly, covering a distance of more than 1,600km. The first breeding record in Britain came from near Cromer, Norfolk, in 1955 but very quickly other low-lying coastal areas were colonised. Most of the initial spread was linked to rural villages and town suburbs, reflecting the association between this species and Man.

That the Collared Dove has been able to spread so widely and so successfully in Britain and Ireland is probably due to a lack of competition with other species already here. The Collared Dove has found a vacant niche, not occupied by another species, and has been able to exploit this. The movement out from the traditional dry habitats of Turkey and the Balkans and into the cooler, wetter climate of more northerly regions has required something of a change in behaviour and habitat use. In countries like Britain and Ireland, the species associates much more closely with human habitation than it does within its former range. Of particular importance appears to be access to grain, either spilt on farmland or provided at suburban bird tables. The importance of cereals in the diet also explains the large flocks which gather outside the breeding season. Collared Doves will also make use of other plant material, like seeds and berries, and will feed as happily on garden plants, as they do on arable weeds.

Another factor in the success of the Collared Dove has been its breeding ecology, in particular its long breeding season and the tendency to start a new breeding attempt before the previous one has been completed. There are instances reported where incubating female Collared Doves use their 'off-duty' breaks from incubation to attend to the recently fledged young of the previous brood. The main breeding season within Britain extends from mid-February through to early October but they have been reported nesting in Christmas trees before Twelfth Night. The nest, a pathetic platform of twigs, is usually placed in a tree or shrub, but may sometimes be built on a ledge or some similar structure. Pairs nesting in suburban habitats are, on average, less successful in their breeding attempts than those in rural areas, but the large number of nesting attempts that can be made during the course of the breeding season result in the production of enough fledged young to ensure that the population keeps

Collared Dove
by Tommy Holden

increasing. During the course of one breeding season, one urban nesting pair of Collared Doves was found to have made seven separate nesting attempts, most of which failed.

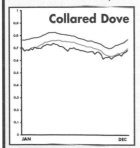

Mortality rates can be quite high, especially among young birds, where over two-thirds of individuals may die during the course of a year. Some of the mortality in rural areas is down to shooting, a relatively recent mortality factor because the species was legally protected in England and Wales up until 1977 and in Scotland up until 1967. Within urban areas, Collared Doves are often predated by Sparrowhawks and cats, something that has led them to favour dense conifers and holly bushes as winter roost sites. Collared Doves appear to be particularly prone to certain diseases and sick or dying individuals are commonly reported by Garden BirdWatchers.

Collared Doves by Tommy Holden

Male Collared Doves defend small territories around the nest by keeping watch for other males from a suitable vantage point. In addition, the male will advertise ownership of the territory by giving a display flight. Like the Woodpigeon, this consists of a steep climb followed by a glide, although the glide is often spiral in nature in the Collared Dove, with tail well spread. An 'excitement' call may also be uttered and this has been best described as a rather jarring 'rrräh'. The more familiar, and rather monotonous, 'ku-koo-ku' call also has a territorial function and is often unpopular with people attempting to sleep through the dawn chorus.

Partitioning resources and habitats

The three species of pigeon found in Garden BirdWatch gardens show some interesting differences in their annual reporting rates. Collared Doves are now the most commonly reported of the three species, with their highest reporting rates, throughout the year, in suburban gardens. The Woodpigeon reporting rate is highest in suburban gardens, for most of the year, although in autumn it is higher in rural gardens. As expected, the Feral Pigeon reporting rate is highest in urban gardens and lowest in rural ones. Although all three species compete for broadly the same types of food, their differing use of urban, rural and suburban gardens helps to reduce the level of competition.

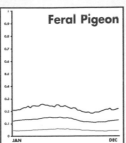

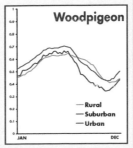

Status
Green listed.
Population has increased since 1950s.

Foods
Grain, seeds, fruit, bread, insects and plant material.

Breeding
Clutch size: 2
Incubates: 13–15 days
Young in nest: c.21 days
No. broods: 3–5
Season: Feb–Oct

Seasonality

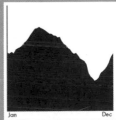

Tawny Owl

Status

Green listed. May be undergoing shallow decline.

Foods

Small mammals, birds, earthworms and frogs.

Breeding

Clutch size: 2–5
Incubates: 28–30 days
Young in nest: 32–35 days
No. broods: 1
Season: Feb–Jun

Seasonality

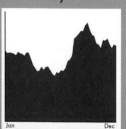

Jan   Dec

This is the owl most likely to be reported using large gardens, churchyards and parks, reflecting its ability to exploit a wide range of prey species. Even so, the reporting rate from Garden BirdWatch gardens is very low, averaging about 3%, with a peak from late autumn through into the winter, when the owls are very vocal in defence of their territories. Tawny Owls are absent from Ireland, the Isle of Man and most of the other islands around our coast.

Tawny Owls generally spend the daylight hours roosting in trees, often against the trunk or amongst ivy. This makes them difficult to spot, so they only tend to be recorded when their characteristic 'tu-weet' and 'tu-woo' calls are made. The males and females utter a range of different calls, though both make the 'ke-wick' contact call that can often be heard through the dark winter months. Tawny Owls are primarily woodland birds, feeding on small mammals and occasionally taking birds. In urban areas there are not the numbers of mice and voles to support them, so brown rats, grey squirrels, Starlings and House Sparrows are taken more often. These are taken at night, the owl using its very sensitive hearing and vision to drop on a prey item from a favoured perch or to dive into bushes occupied by roosting birds. Tawny Owls will hunt on foot, coming down to feed on earthworms in much the same way as Blackbirds do.

Tawny Owls need to find a suitable cavity in which to nest. These cavities are often surprisingly open and this may explain why Tawny Owls will also take over the large stick nests of crows and Sparrowhawks. Young Tawny Owls leave the nest well before they are able to fly. They clamber about in the branches and occasionally fall to the ground, where they are sometimes found by garden birdwatchers. Unless the youngster is in immediate danger of being taken by a cat, it is best to leave it where found. Youngsters are quite capable of climbing back up tree trunks by using their incredibly strong claws.

Adult females are very good parents and can be aggressive at the nest. A well-known photographer, the late Eric Hosking, lost an eye to a Tawny Owl early in his career. Evidence suggests that Tawny Owls nesting in well-populated areas may be more aggressive than those breeding in more remote locations.

If you are lucky enough to see a Tawny Owl, then you will notice that it has short, broad wings and tail, features that help it to manoeuvre through its preferred woodland habitat. Owls that hunt on the wing in open country, like the Barn Owl, have longer wings. The Tawny Owl's plumage is a streaky brown colour and the eyes are black, standing out against the pale facial disc.

Tawny Owl by Jill Pakenham

Swifts are one of the last of our summer migrants to arrive and first to depart, typically arriving in late April and remaining here for just 16 weeks. Not all of the Swifts that arrive for the summer are here to breed; many are young birds that won't nest for their first few summers. A delay in reaching breeding age is unusual in a small bird because of the high levels of mortality that small birds usually suffer. It should be no surprise, therefore, that only one in six adults die in a given year, a much lower figure than that for similarly sized birds.

Within Britain and Ireland, nests are placed under eaves in a cavity in a building or in a specially designed nestbox. In parts of eastern Europe, Swifts prefer tree cavities or crevices in cliff faces. Old buildings are favoured over more modern constructions because modern houses lack the access under the eaves that Swifts require. Swifts seem to favour tall buildings because the extra height allows them to drop from the nest site and reach sufficient speed to get airborne. Grounded Swifts find it particularly difficult to get into the air and, apart from when visiting the nest, they never willingly land. Non-breeding birds roost on the wing during the breeding season, gathering together in an evening ascent that takes them to higher altitudes, where they appear to sleep whilst using a gliding flight.

The first pairs to breed will typically lay three eggs, those starting later just two. The weather conditions, and hence the availability of aerial insects, determines not only when breeding starts but also how long it takes. During wet or windy conditions, Swifts may find it difficult to find food for their developing chicks. The chicks can cope with this to some extent by going into a torpor, which may last for several days if the weather is bad. The consequence of this is that chicks can take between 35 and 56 days to fledge from the nest. Once they leave, they are fully independent and depart for their wintering grounds in Africa within a few days. One ringed chick that left its nest in Britain was killed in Madrid four days later. The adults remain for a few days longer and then depart south. Although the two birds that make up a breeding pair may have no contact with each other outside of the breeding season, they invariably return to the same breeding site, maintaining the pair bond from one year to the next.

Summer

Winter

Status
Green listed.
Population trend largely unknown.

Foods
Flying insects and airborne spiders.

Breeding
Clutch size: 2–3
Incubates: 12–18 days
Young in nest: 35–56 days
No. broods: 1
Season: May–Aug

Seasonality

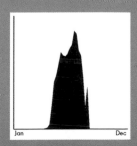

Jan   Dec

These nesting Swifts were photographed using an in-nestbox camera as part of a project being carried out by BTO-ringer Graham Roberts. Graham's work on Swifts, in his loft in Portsmouth, has provided some unique insights into the breeding ecology of this species.

Swifts by Graham Roberts

Kingfisher

Status

Amber Listed. No clear long-term trend in numbers.

Foods

Fish and aquatic invertebrates, amphibians.

Breeding

Clutch size: 5–8
Incubates: 19–20 days
Young in nest: 23–27 days
No. broods: 2
Season: Mar–Sep

Seasonality

Sample size currently too small to produce a seasonality plot.

Although the Kingfisher cannot be described as a regular garden bird, some lucky Garden BirdWatchers report Kingfishers in their gardens every week. During severe winter weather, when water bodies freeze over and Kingfishers are unable to reach their favoured food, some individuals will take kitchen scraps from bird tables in gardens close to rivers, lakes and streams. Birds have been recorded taking offal, suet and even bread, highlighting the tremendous difficulties they face in very cold winters. Results from the BTO's Waterways Bird Survey have highlighted the effect that severe winters, such as 1981/82, can have on the Kingfisher population, sometimes resulting in the local extinction of the species from affected areas.

Dispersing birds travel cross-country and can turn up at gardens virtually anywhere. Kingfishers may be more regular visitors to garden ponds if these happen to be within a few hundred metres of a larger body of water. The presence of a good stock of small fish and a suitable perch from which to hunt are essential. A perch that is between one and two metres above the water is favoured, since this provides an ideal vantage point from which to spot prey. Once the Kingfisher has selected a likely target, it will bob its head up and down to better gauge the position of the fish. The bird will then dive headlong into the water, holding its wings open underwater and protecting its eyes with a special third nictitating eyelid. These dives can take the bird to depths of 25cm, quite deep for a small bird. The Kingfisher then struggles free from the water and will often return to the perch, to perform the delicate juggling act of getting the fish into a head-down position from which it can be swallowed.

Kingfishers nest in burrows, typically excavated in soft riverbanks and up to 140cm in length, the tunnel rising slightly along its length to the circular nesting chamber. The construction of such a long tunnel is a difficult task for a bird and takes many days. Several weeks after the eggs hatch, the young emerge and begin a noisy exploration of their surroundings. It is often at this stage that Kingfishers are at their most obvious. Kingfishers invariably raise their second brood in a new nest tunnel, understandable when one considers the stinking mess left in the first nest following a diet largely composed of fish!

Improving water quality has benefited the Kingfisher, by allowing populations of small fish (typically minnows, sticklebacks and small trout) to return to once-polluted streams and rivers. This has enabled Kingfishers to colonise some urban areas, giving the chance for more people to witness the bright blue blur of a Kingfisher disappearing up-river from a favoured perch.

Kingfisher by Colin Varndell

The Ring-necked Parakeet is the most colourful species to visit garden bird feeding stations on a regular basis. Unlike many other exotic birds that are occasional escapees from aviaries and private collections, the Ring-necked Parakeet has managed to establish a sizeable breeding population, centred on the Home Counties and the Thames Valley. There are also small breeding populations in Germany, Belgium and several other countries. Breeding in the wild in Britain was first reported in 1969 and the population is now thought to number many thousands of individuals, mainly breeding in larger gardens and parks throughout the suburban parts of Surrey and Kent.

It is during the early winter months that the size of the Ring-necked Parakeet population can best be assessed. At this time of the year, the birds gather together in large roosts at favoured sites. One such roost, in Surrey, recently held over 6,000 birds during one night. The birds arrive at the roosts before dark, when they are particularly vocal. The parakeets forage in smaller parties during the day and early in the winter favour apples still on the trees. Annoyingly, they never seem to consume whole apples, preferring to take a few pecks before moving on to another. Later in the winter, food provided at bird tables and in hanging feeders is important, helping these birds get through the winter. Certainly, severe weather, such as that of the 1981/82 winter, does not seem to have checked their population – our birds derive from the montane Indian race and are pre-adapted to cold nights. It appears that the Ring-necked Parakeet is here to stay, which raises the question of whether it will become a significant pest of major economic importance in orchards.

We need to find out how the spread of Ring-necked Parakeets is affecting other bird species. These parakeets are cavity nesters and often take over old woodpecker holes, putting them in direct competition with species like Little Owl and Jackdaw. Not only are Ring-necked Parakeets aggressive but they also take up residence very early in the year. Winter roosts break up soon after Christmas, as individuals begin to pair up, with egg-laying initiated from January onwards. Other parrot species have also succeeded in breeding in the wild within Britain and these populations also need to be monitored on a regular basis to see if they become established.

Summer

Winter

Status
Green listed. Population increasing away from core range in southern England.

Foods
Omnivorous, taking fruit, seeds and plant material.

Breeding
Clutch size: 3–4
Incubates: 22–24 days
Young in nest: 40–50 days
No. broods: 1
Season: Jan–Aug

Seasonality

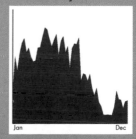

Native to Africa and Asia, Ring-necked Parakeets are attractive birds, yellowish green in colour with a long tail, rosehip red beak and a pink neck collar in the male. Adult birds have the longest tails. In flight, the dark underwing feathers can be seen. The calls made are very loud and squawking in nature. Alexandrine Parakeets are also established in Britain.

Ring-necked Parakeet by Mike Weston

Summer

Winter

Status

Amber listed. Steady long-term increase.

Foods

Largely adult and larval ants.

Breeding

Clutch size: 5–7

Incubates: 18–19 days

Young in nest: 18–21 days

No. broods: 1

Season: Apr–Jul

Seasonality

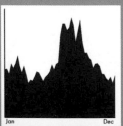

Jan   Dec

The Green Woodpecker, unmistakeable with its bright green plumage, yellow rump and red crown, is an occasional visitor to gardens, chiefly to lawns and rarely to bird tables. It is the largest of our woodpeckers and spends a great deal of time away from trees, foraging on the ground, where it feeds upon ants, taking adults, larvae and eggs from their nests. To help with this choice of diet, the Green Woodpecker has an extremely long tongue that can be extended to a length of just over 10cm. The tip of the tongue is wide and flat, extremely mobile and covered with sticky saliva produced by the enlarged salivary glands. Green Woodpeckers are often found foraging in areas of old pasture and dry heath, where ant colonies thrive, as well as in woodland glades and on garden lawns. During the summer months, birds seem to take smaller ant species but later in the year they tend to take larger more conspicuous species, often exploiting other habitats like golf courses and parks. In the winter, ants can be difficult to find, especially when there is deep snow cover or hard frosts. As a consequence, during particularly bad winters the Green Woodpecker population may decline dramatically.

The bill of the Green Woodpecker is weaker than that of other woodpecker species. It is usually only used to chisel on soft wood, which explains why Green Woodpeckers do not often drum on tree trunks. They make up for this by being particularly vocal; the very loud, laughing call gives the bird its local name of 'yaffle' and is a familiar sound to most users of the countryside.

Although the Green Woodpecker has been extending its range in Britain (breeding for the first time in Scotland in 1951), it is absent from Ireland (there are just three very old records) and the Isle of Man, and is most abundant in the southeast of Britain. During a 20–year period of range expansion, the species spread some 200km further north, despite being a rather sedentary species. Green Woodpeckers also appear reluctant to cross large water bodies, the Isle of Wight not being colonised until 1910.

Green Woodpeckers do not usually take food provided at bird tables or feeders but they have been recorded taking fat, fruit and mealworms provided on the ground.

Green Woodpeckers are quite easy to age and sex. Young birds usually have some grey showing among the red crown feathers, while adults have all red crowns. Males (inset) have red moustachial stripes that extend down under the black patch that surrounds the eye, though this is reduced in young males. In females (main picture), the stripe is black.

Green Woodpeckers by Darren Frost & Colin Varndell

The Great Spotted Woodpecker is the larger of our two black and white woodpeckers, being about the size of a Starling (the Lesser-spotted is about the size of a sparrow). It is also the most widespread and a regular visitor to many garden feeding stations. The Great Spotted Woodpecker population increased throughout the 20th Century and the species is now common in suburban parks and gardens. Even so, it is more of a woodland specialist than the Green Woodpecker. The species is absent from higher ground within Scotland and from Ireland and the Isle of Man.

Perhaps surprisingly for a bird seemingly adapted to extract invertebrates living inside dead and dying wood, the Great Spotted Woodpecker eats a lot of tree seeds. These are of particular importance during the winter, when the birds favour the seeds of pine and spruce, though they will also take those of oak, beech and hazel. Sometimes the seeds are wedged into the bark of trees and then hammered open with the chisel-like bill. This bill is adapted for getting into dead wood to reach insects but it also allows the woodpecker to 'drum', producing a sound that can be heard over long distances. Drumming is most often heard between March and May. Both sexes drum. A loud, distinctive 'tchick' call may also be heard from time to time.

Young Great Spotted Woodpeckers can be very noisy in the nest, where they are often fed on a diet of moth larvae. When they leave the nest hole during early summer there is an increase in the Garden BirdWatch reporting rate, as adults bring their young to garden feeding stations. Peanuts are a favoured food, nutritionally similar to many tree seeds, and visits to hanging feeders by family parties provide an excellent opportunity to try your identification skills (see below). Later in the year these family parties break up and the young move away. While all woodpeckers are predominantly sedentary in lifestyle, the Great Spotted Woodpecker does show a greater degree of movement than most. British Great Spotted Woodpeckers don't tend to move far but those from populations living in the northern pine forests of Scandinavia show eruptive movements when the seed crops fail. Such movements bring a small number of birds from Scandinavia to Britain each autumn and periodically there are much larger influxes – the most recent of which was in 1974 (Scotland).

Summer

Winter

Status
Green listed. Has been increasing in recent years.

Foods
Mainly insects and tree seeds. Also eggs & young birds from nestboxes.

Breeding
Clutch size: 4–7
Incubates: 16–18 days
Young in nest: 18–21 days
No. broods: 1
Season: Apr–Jul

Seasonality

Jan　　　　　　Dec

The juvenile (top left) has a red crown and pale red colouration under the tail. The adult male (right) has a red patch on the back of the head and bright red under tail coverts. The adult female (bottom left) also has this bright red undertail but lacks any red on the head. All ages of the Lesser Spotted Woodpecker lack any red under the tail.

Great Spotted Woodpeckers by Tommy Holden & George Higginbotham

Swallow

Summer

Winter

The Swallow must be the most familiar of our summer visitors, one of the first to arrive and last to leave. In Britain and Ireland, Swallows are strongly associated with Man and virtually all nests are built within man-made structures, such as barns, porches and outhouses. The most favoured sites are often those in old farm buildings with livestock present, set within landscapes where large aerial insects are abundant. Because of the types of site used and a diet centred on aerial insects, the Swallow can be found over most of Britain and Ireland, being absent only from the centres of towns and high uplands.

Swallow populations are known to fluctuate from one year to the next, especially at the local level, and this is most probably the result of mortality occurring during migration or on the African wintering grounds. Swallows undertake incredible journeys for such small birds (it is something like 6,000 miles to South Africa where many winter) and do so year after year. Behind these annual fluctuations there appears to be a longer-term decline but the population may have recovered somewhat during recent years.

Swallow nests are made from pellets of mud, collected and mixed with saliva and fibrous material to give the nest rigidity. Many of the nests will last more than one season and both birds from a pair may return to occupy a nest used during a previous year. The male usually arrives before the female and will either begin to construct a new nest or make repairs to an existing one, leaving the female to take over when she arrives. During the course of building the nest, birds may collect more than 1,000 separate mud pellets. Many pairs manage to raise two broods, while some successfully rear three. This is one of the reasons why they are one of the last migrants to leave Britain and Ireland. If suitable nest sites are available then Swallows may nest in small groups, although the individual pair defends the area around its own nest and they cannot really be regarded as being colonial. The newly-fledged young will remain around the breeding site, being fed by their parents, for up to six weeks but are often chased away by the male earlier than this. Once they leave the local area these youngsters join large communal roosts, where they will remain until the southward migration begins.

Adult Swallow (in flight) feeding young by Tommy Holden

Most Swallows leave Britain and Ireland during September and October, heading south through Europe and into North Africa, where they cross the Sahara. During November our Swallows finally reach their wintering grounds in South Africa, where they will remain until February. The return journey follows the reverse route and brings the first breeding birds back into southern Britain during March. Poor weather conditions along the route, especially cold and wet weather, can cause serious losses. The first returning birds often face relatively poor conditions on the breeding grounds and may search for prey over water, where flying insects tend to be more abundant. The birds may also associate with livestock, since cattle and horses often disturb flies from the vegetation in which they feed. Changing farming practices, including more intensive stock rearing, modern buildings, pesticides and improved farm hygiene, may exert an impact on breeding populations of Swallows, by reducing the abundance of suitable insect prey. There is certainly evidence of a long-term decline in the abundance of flying insects within parts of Britain.

The long tail feathers of adult Swallows play an important role in mate selection. Research has demonstrated that female Swallows find males with the longest tail feathers the most attractive. These males preferentially acquire mates earlier than males with shorter tail feathers and, importantly, they also enjoy higher breeding success. It is thought that such adornments sported by the males of some species are a true indication of the 'fitness' of a male. The females can then use these features to select the best mates. Young birds lack the long-streamers and the rufous colouring is less strongly marked than in the adults. Swallows of all ages lack the white rump that is characteristic of the House Martin. The flight is swift, low and with lots of banking and turning as they search for large flies.

Migration Watch

Migration Watch is one of the BTO's online surveys and is used to gather information on the arrival patterns of spring migrants. Sightings of migrants submitted over the Internet are analysed overnight, allowing up-to-date maps to be published the following day. The arrival of Swallows during spring 2003 is shown in the maps presented below. These three, weekly maps demonstrate just how quickly the main influx moves across the country.

The Migration Watch project is open to anyone with access to the Internet and can be reached via the BTO's Home Page at www.bto.org. The Migration Watch pages also contain results and maps for the years during which the project has been running.

| 30 March 2003 | 6 April 2003 | 13 April 2003 |

Status
Amber listed. Long-term decline with recent increase.

Foods
Aerial insects.

Breeding
Clutch size: 4–6
Incubates: 14–16 days
Young in nest: 17–24 days
No. broods: 1–3
Season: Mar–Oct

Seasonality

Jan   Dec

Summer

Winter

Status

Green listed. Long-term trend is stable.

Foods

Aphids and other small flying insects.

Breeding

Clutch size: 4–5

Incubates: 14–16 days

Young in nest: 16–22 days

No. broods: 2 (3)

Season: Apr–Sep

Seasonality

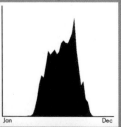

The House Martin shows a very close association with Man, building its familiar mud nests under the eaves of houses, outbuildings and other Man-made structures (*e.g.* bridges). These nests are usually placed in colonies, which can contain up to several hundred pairs. Colonies established in urban areas are generally smaller than those in the suburbs, which in turn are smaller than colonies in rural areas. One might imagine that House Martins compete for aerial insects with Swallows, Swifts and Sand Martins. To some extent they do, but the different species tend to feed at different heights and on differently-sized insects, thus reducing the degree of competition.

House Martins are summer visitors and the main influx into the country occurs during the second half of April and early May. In common with many other migrants, males tend to arrive back before females and older birds return before young birds. The older birds usually occupy old nests and, while a few running repairs may be needed, they are spared the arduous task of building a nest from scratch. The nests are made from mud and are built from the base up over a period of one to two weeks. During periods of very dry weather, the birds can have difficulty in finding sources of mud. The males are surprisingly aggressive in the defence of their small nest territories but they sometimes lose out to House Sparrows, which will take over nearly completed nests. Most House Martins usually go on to rear a second brood (very few manage three) and are helped on occasion by young from the first brood. This helps to ensure that the young from the second brood receive sufficient food to fledge before the summer ends, while at the same time giving the young from the first brood some experience in rearing chicks. A few birds manage to breed aged up to six years, although they rarely live longer than this.

Even though large numbers of House Martins have been ringed in Britain and Ireland, we still know surprisingly little about where they spend the winter. Results from ringing right across Europe have highlighted that House Martins winter in Africa, south of the Sahara, but we do not know the exact wintering locations of birds from the different breeding populations. It has been suggested that the birds may remain on the wing, feeding above the equatorial forest canopy, where they do not come into contact with Man.

The House Martin has a shiny blue-black and white plumage with a white rump. This white rump is distinctive and is absent from our other swallows and martins. In dry summers, House Martins can be helped by creating mud 'puddles' to provide a source of mud for nest-building.

House Martin by Derek Belsey

With its black and white plumage and constantly wagging tail, the Pied Wagtail is familiar to most garden birdwatchers. The Pied Wagtail is actually the British and Irish race of the White Wagtail which breeds elsewhere in Europe (and sporadically here). Pied Wagtails in southern Britain are mostly sedentary but many of those from northern Britain move south to winter in southern Britain and along the Atlantic coasts of France and Spain.

Pied Wagtails utilise a wide range of habitats and are even found nesting in the middle of our largest urban centres. Wagtails specialise in feeding on insects, especially small flies like midges, often taken at the water's edge. During the late autumn, they may also be seen at garden feeding stations taking seeds and even bread, foods that will be additional to the insects upon which they are likely to be concentrating. During the winter months, things become more difficult because insects become less abundant. It has been discovered that Pied Wagtails may spend more than 90% of the short winter daylight hours feeding, taking a small prey item every three to four seconds. Even this concentrated effort may not be enough to meet the energy requirements of the bird and this may be why northern populations tend to migrate south for the winter, where temperatures may be higher and prey more abundant. Adult males establish feeding territories in the winter and, if sufficient food is available within them, may tolerate the presence of females or immatures. These 'satellite' birds help to defend the territory against other birds, but are soon chased off if food availability declines. Other birds remain in feeding flocks that are more mobile. Pied Wagtails can often be seen walking about, occasionally pecking some prey item from the ground but on other occasions making a darting run to grab something that has caught their eye. They may also 'flycatch' from a suitable perch.

Another feature of the winter ecology of this species is the large communal roosts that can gather at favoured sites. Hundreds of individuals may congregate to roost in reed beds, around buildings such as hospitals and supermarkets or in large commercial greenhouses. Such roosting sites may provide some protection from predators, allow individuals to follow others to better feeding grounds or be warmer than surrounding habitat.

Summer

Winter

Status

Green listed. Long-term trend currently stable.

Foods

Small invertebrates, fat, fine seeds in winter.

Breeding

Clutch size: 5–6
Incubates: 13–14 days
Young in nest: 14–16 days
No. broods: 2 (3)
Season: Apr–Aug

Seasonality

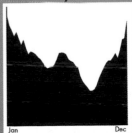

Jan — Dec

The Pied Wagtail's nest is a cup of twigs and grass stems, lined with wool, hair and feathers, and placed in a wide variety of recesses, including the walls of old houses and outbuildings. The species can sometimes be tempted to nest in open fronted nestboxes of the type used for Robins. Large gardens, close to running water, are favoured.

Pied Wagtail by Tommy Holden

Summer

Winter

In most of its European range the Dunnock is found on mountain slopes, in scrubby vegetation close to the tree line. It is only in Britain and Ireland, together with a few areas within Central Europe and the Netherlands, that this species has established itself as a garden bird. Here, Dunnocks are usually to be seen under bushes or below the bird table, foraging with mouse-like movements as they search for insects and small seeds. They rarely venture onto hanging feeders but will visit raised bird tables. These unobtrusive little birds used to be called 'Hedge Sparrows' but, while they do favour hedges and other low cover, they are certainly not sparrows. They may share a drab brown plumage with the House Sparrow but the shape of their bill is very different, being sharp and pointed – ideal for picking up very small seeds or insects.

There has been a steady but shallow decline in the size of the British and Irish population over recent decades and this is mirrored in the Garden Bird Feeding Survey results. Dunnocks are found right across Britain and Ireland, although in the remoter parts of the north and west they are common only in gardens, where thick cover is available. This cover is used for nesting and the nest is usually well camouflaged and difficult to locate. A foundation of small twigs supports the exquisite open cup of moss and leaves into which the deep blue eggs are laid. The Dunnock is the main host for the Cuckoo in gardens but, because female Cuckoos do not yet produce eggs that mimic the Dunnock's blue eggs, it is considered to be a relatively recent host. This is supported by the fact that parasitized Dunnocks do not reject the Cuckoo egg from their nest, even though it does not resemble their own eggs.

The Garden BirdWatch reporting rate reveals something of the Dunnock's very complex social system. Although most Dunnocks living in gardens are monogamous, with a male and female making up a pair, others engage in more complicated relationships. For example, polyandry (one female with two males) is quite common, polygyny (one male with two or more females) is regular and even polygynandry (two or three males with three or four females) can sometimes occur. These unusual groupings seem to result from the fact that male and female Dunnocks maintain their own largely independent territories during the breeding season. Male territories are typically larger than those of the females and this means that the territory of a male may overlap the territories of two or more females. This could give rise to polygyny. However, the situation is even more complex than this because some male territories are shared by two males, one of whom (the alpha male) is dominant over the other (the beta male). The beta male seems to secure his position within the territory of the alpha

*Dunnock by
John Harding*

male through sheer persistence. Both males may mate with the same female, although the alpha male spends a lot of his time guarding his female as she approaches the egg-laying period and so the beta male may fail to secure a successful mating. It is this mate-guarding behaviour which results in the peak in the Garden BirdWatch reporting rate for Dunnock pairs during March.

An elaborate pre-copulation display has evolved because of the complex social system. Prior to copulation the female will crouch low in front of the male and quiver, whilst at the same time fluffing up her body feathers and lifting her tail. The male, positioned behind the female, then hops from side to side and pecks at the female's cloaca. This pecking may continue for up to two minutes, during which time the cloaca becomes pink and enlarged, often making strong pumping movements and sometimes ejecting some of the sperm from a previous mating. The pecking which results in the ejection of sperm from a previous mating is the male's way of attempting to increase his share of the paternity. If an alpha male notices that another male has been near his mate, he will spend longer on the pre-copulation pecking. Another display that is sometimes seen involves several birds gathered together, flicking their wings. This is part of a territory dispute between neighbouring males, with both alpha and beta males defending 'their' territory. Interestingly, both alpha and beta males will sing within the territory as well, again suggesting mutual defence of the territory.

Dunnocks are usually solitary in the winter, though several individuals may gather together at a rich food source, *e.g.* in the vicinity of a garden feeding station. Female birds present in such groups remain subordinate to the males and are sometimes forced to move further afield in search of food. It is thought that in harsh winters, away from gardens, females may suffer higher levels of mortality and that in the following breeding season this will give rise to the more complex pairings. In gardens, where food may not be limiting because of year round feeding, females may be able to establish smaller territories than they could elsewhere. This is more likely to give rise to a monogamous pairing, since one male can better guard a female if she has a small territory.

Status

Amber listed. Shallow decline in gardens.

Foods

Small seeds, insects, spiders, breadcrumbs and grated cheese.

Breeding

Clutch size: 4–5
Incubates: c.12 days
Young in nest: c.12 days
No. broods: 2–3
Season: Mar–Aug

Seasonality

During the winter months Dunnocks take more small seeds and fewer insects and spiders. They also take peanut fragments, finely grated cheese, bread-crumbs and nyjer seed and have even been recorded taking fat, small pieces of meat and various berries.

Dunnock by Tommy Holden

Blackbird

Summer

Winter

*Female Blackbird
by Tommy Holden*

The Blackbird is one of the dominant species in gardens and has been recorded making up as much as 50% of the bird community in some urban studies. Originally the Blackbird was a species of high forest but, within Britain, the gradual spread into man-made habitats began during the 19th Century and was seemingly completed in the early part of the 20th Century. This ability to occupy such a wide range of habitats, especially man-made ones, reflects the adaptable nature of this familiar thrush. Recent analyses suggest that as much as 27% of the British and Irish Blackbird population may now occur within human habitats, existing at densities of around 100 birds per km^2, which highlights the importance of urban and suburban parks and gardens. Recent research has revealed that Blackbirds nesting in towns and villages are more productive than those in woodland, with the rate of nest predation in gardens (50%) being considerably lower than that in woodland (80%). Woodland populations have to contend with crows, Magpies, Jays, grey squirrels and weasels, all important nest predators, while in gardens only the domestic cat and Magpie are real threats. The most serious problem in gardens, during the nesting period at least, is that of starvation of the nestlings during dry periods, when earthworms become difficult to extract from parched lawns. Even allowing for this, and the slightly higher mortality levels that fledged young suffer, suburban populations of Blackbirds are thought to act as a source from which birds can enter the less productive woodland population.

Much of our understanding of Blackbird ecology and behaviour comes from studies carried out in urban and suburban parks and gardens, where traditional breeding and feeding sites are occupied year after year by well-established and dominant birds. Food is usually readily available throughout the year, partly a consequence of the catholic diet of the species, and birds can maintain compact and tightly packed territories. The Garden BirdWatch reporting rate shows a pronounced seasonal cycle which is even more interesting when broken down into different 'flock size' categories. During early spring there is a peak in the reporting rate for pairs. Sightings of single birds peak in late summer, a time when the overall reporting rate drops, matching the period during which individuals may leave gardens, to feed elsewhere on fruiting trees and shrubs, or skulk under bushes as they undergo the moult of their feathers. The reporting rate for larger groups of birds shows two peaks during the course of the year. One, in mid summer, relates to family parties, the other occurs in the winter, corresponding with the arrival of immigrants.

It has been estimated, from bird ringing data, that at least 12% of the Blackbirds present in Britain and Ireland during the winter are immigrants from elsewhere in Europe. Our own breeding birds are resident although, following a run of cold winters earlier last century, some from breeding populations in northern England and Scotland undertook regular movements to winter in Ireland. Winter immigrants have been shown to originate in countries including Finland, Sweden, Denmark and the Netherlands. Some of these birds pass through eastern England during October to winter further south in France, Spain and Portugal. Others arrive slightly later, to forage alongside our resident birds in orchards and gardens on windfall apples and kitchen scraps. Although it is not possible to identify with certainty which are residents and which are immigrants in the winter, by March, when resident males acquire their breeding plumage, the two groups can be told apart. Our resident breeding males will have orange-yellow bills and eye rings, while immigrant males won't get theirs until they return to their European breeding grounds. Thomas Hardy, who described the bill as being 'crocus coloured', best captured the warmth of the yellow tones. The Garden BirdWatch team often receive reports of Blackbirds, particularly older males, that have partly white plumage. The amount of white sometimes appears to increase each year after the bird has moulted. It is likely that the presence of these white feathers has a genetic basis, since the occurrence of these partial albinos may be common in some localities.

Adult male (top) and juvenile male (bottom) by Tommy Holden

Status

Amber listed.
Population in decline.

Foods

Insects, earthworms and fruit.

Breeding

Clutch size: 3–5
Incubates: 12–15 days
Young in nest: 12–15 days
No. broods: 2–5
Season: Mar–Sep

Seasonality

In decline

Blackbird populations in farmland have fallen by about 30% since the early 1970s, possibly a result of changes in agricultural practices. However, both the Garden Bird Feeding Survey (below) and Garden BirdWatch reporting rates suggest that populations in rural (green) and suburban (blue) gardens are currently stable.

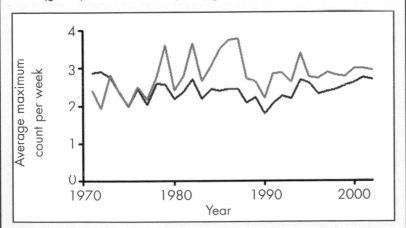

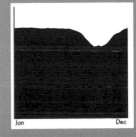

Song Thrush

The lawns and shrubberies of a typical garden are ideal for the Song Thrush, providing both feeding opportunities and thick cover for nesting. The suitability of gardens for Song Thrushes is highlighted by the fact that habitats associated with human habitation hold just under a quarter of the entire British Song Thrush population. Densities in these habitats average some 10 birds per km², similar to those in woodland and far greater than those reported from farmland. With Song Thrush populations known to be in decline in farmland, this makes gardens all the more important for this species. Song Thrushes are present in about 35% of Garden BirdWatch gardens during the early part of the summer.

The decline of the Song Thrush, which began in the mid–1970s, has been monitored by the BTO through its Common Birds Census and, more recently, through the Breeding Bird Survey. The rapidity of the decline (some 57% over 31 years) has earned the Song Thrush its place on the 'Red list', as a species of high conservation concern. During the early decades of the 20th Century, Song Thrushes were more abundant than Blackbirds but since the 1940s Blackbirds have been the commoner of the two. In rural areas there are now nine Blackbirds for every Song Thrush and in urban areas it is more like 12 Blackbirds for every Song Thrush. The average Garden BirdWatch reporting rate for Song Thrush is much lower than that for Blackbird, which is usually over 90%. There is a degree of competition between these two species and other thrushes in winter.

Song Thrushes generally choose to nest in thick cover, typically bushes and shrubs, some two metres or so off the ground. The nest is similar to that made by other thrushes but the mud lining is pressed smooth by the female using her breast. Song Thrushes can pair as early as the end of February in southern England and are monogamous. The breeding season can last into September, by which stage two or even three broods may have been raised. The Song Thrush is a familiar bird to most garden birdwatchers, although some observers may find it difficult to separate this species from its relative the Mistle Thrush (see identification features beginning on page 119).

Many people associate Song Thrushes with the habit of smashing open snail shells. Interestingly, snails are only an important food source for Song Thrushes at certain times of year. During the early part of the breeding season (March–May), Song Thrushes mainly feed on earthworms but by early June they may have switched their attentions to caterpillars. It is only really in late summer that snails become important, as other foods become hard to find. This is particularly true in hot dry spells when earthworms retreat deep into the soil. Snails can also be important during cold winters, when frozen ground restricts access to earthworms. The Song Thrush has developed a rather clever technique for dealing with snails.

Song Thrush anvil by Mike Toms

The bird usually grabs hold of the snail by the lip of the shell, before carrying it to a favoured stone which it uses as an anvil. The impact typically only removes part of the shell but this still allows the bird to extract the snail's body which is then wiped on the ground before being eaten. Other thrushes do not normally feed on snails in this manner.

It has been suggested that the use of slug pellets is one of the reasons for the decline in Song Thrushes and, while we don't have any direct evidence that this is the case, many wildlife gardeners avoid their use, not least

Song Thrush by Dick Jeeves

because they are toxic to other animals, including household pets. We know, from work carried out at the BTO, that increased mortality of young Song Thrushes, particularly in the first few months after they fledge, is likely to have caused the population decline. What is not clear is why these youngsters are failing to survive. It may be that the increased use of slug pellets and lawn treatments has reduced the availability of snails or earthworms at a time of year when other foods are difficult to find.

Information on the BTO ring-recovery database shows that most Song Thrushes move less than a kilometre between where they are ringed and where they are recovered. However, some birds from northern Britain move south for the winter. This type of pattern, where only part of the population migrates, is known as partial migration. Typically, such birds will migrate either because the weather conditions would be unfavourable were they to remain or because they face tough competition from more dominant individuals or species. The winter Garden BirdWatch reporting rate for Song Thrush is higher in southern Britain than in Scotland.

Status

Red listed. Long-term decline, now stable in gardens.

Foods

Insects, earthworms, snails and fruit.

Breeding

Clutch size: 3–5
Incubates: 12–14 days
Young in nest: c.15 days
No. broods: 2–3
Season: Mar–Sep

Seasonality

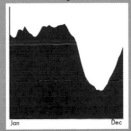

Jan   Dec

Breeding success

Results from the BTO's Nest Record Scheme have revealed an increase in the breeding performance of Song Thrushes over the period in which the population itself has been in decline. This strongly suggests that breeding performance is not the reason behind the decline in Song Thrush numbers

and that factors operating on other aspects of the Song Thrush's life cycle are most likely to be responsible. The use of BTO Nest Records in this way helps to establish the causes behind the declines of different species. If you are interested in becoming involved in the BTO Nest Record Scheme, please see the box on page 22.

Song Thrush at nest by George Higginbotham

Blackcap

Summer

Winter

*Female Blackcap
by Tommy Holden*

Of the various warblers to visit gardens, the Blackcap is perhaps the most familiar. Warblers are small birds that feed primarily on insects, a diet that is reflected in the shape of their bills – thin and pointed is ideal for dealing with insects but less suited to seeds. In fact, the Blackcap is more catholic in its diet than many other warbler species, feeding in winter on fat, bread, fruit and even meat on occasion. The Blackcap differs from many of the other warblers in that it is primarily a winter visitor to Garden BirdWatch gardens, something that is very unusual for a bird commonly regarded as being a summer migrant (see box).

Blackcaps are primarily woodland birds, widely distributed throughout Britain and Ireland but with their highest densities in southern England. As summer migrants, they arrive to breed in Britain at the beginning of April, using habitats with a good shrub layer in which to nest and suitable trees from which the males deliver their rich and measured song. Blackcaps can arrive earlier than many other insect-eating migrants because they are also able to feed on fruit and other foods if insects are unavailable. The females usually arrive a week or two after the males and quickly begin breeding.

Most of the Blackcaps which breed in Britain and Ireland leave during September and October to spend the winter around the western end of the Mediterranean, where they feed on berries taken from a range of shrubs. However, some are present in Britain and Ireland during the winter months and what's more, the number of individuals wintering here appears to be rapidly increasing. This tremendous growth is a recent phenomenon but there are also old winter records going back over a century. Of particular interest for the garden birdwatcher is that gardens, especially suburban ones (as revealed by a BTO wintering Blackcap survey and Garden BirdWatch reporting rates), appear to be a favoured habitat for these wintering birds, especially during hard weather. Amazingly, these are not simply birds that have chosen to remain here (although BTO ringing research has shown that some do remain). Instead, most are from the central European population; birds that have migrated here in the autumn from Germany, Belgium and Switzerland. This implies that there has been a shift in the migratory habits of some of the birds, resulting in a change in where they winter. Pioneering work by Peter Berthold of the Max–Planck Institute in Germany has revealed that this change in behaviour has a genetic basis.

Wintering Blackcaps appear to prefer natural foods like berries but once these become scarce they will take a wide variety of other items. It is well worth providing fats, bread and cheese to see if you can encourage regular visits by Blackcaps between December and March, the period during which the Garden BirdWatch reporting rate increases to 10–15%. Detailed work carried out by bird

ringers has shown that Blackcaps feeding on these foods are able to maintain or even increase their body weight during periods of severe weather. One of the features of visiting Blackcaps, often reported by Garden BirdWatchers, is their aggressive nature around the bird table, with other species often chased away from suitable food sources.

Adult male Blackcaps are unmistakeable, with their dark wings, olive-brown back, grey nape and jet black crown. Adult females sport a rufous-coloured crown and are greyer in colour on their upperparts. Young birds present more of a challenge in that both males and females have brown caps.

Male Blackcap
by Tommy Holden

Blackcap movements in autumn

The general heading of Blackcaps from central Europe in autumn is southwest (a direction of about 230°) but there is quite a bit of variation and some of these birds would normally reach Britain & Ireland. Historically those that did reach our shores would have found conditions unsuitable. In recent decades, however, they have been able to survive, partly due to the milder winters we now have and partly due to the food provided by garden birdwatchers.

These birds appear to arrive back on their central European breeding grounds some two weeks before those individuals that have wintered around the Mediterranean Basin. It is thought that this offers them a competitive advantage, enabling them to raise more youngsters than other birds. This may explain how this behaviour has spread so rapidly through the breeding population. This is a good example of rapid evolutionary change, something that is far more commonly reported in invertebrates and other 'lower' orders of animals.

The map shows British-breeding Blackcaps (red) moving south in the autumn, while some birds from central Europe (blue) are moving into Britain over the same period.

Male Blackcap by Tommy Holden

Status
Green listed.
Population increasing.

Foods
Insects, spiders, fruit, grated cheese and fat

Breeding
Clutch size: 4–5
Incubates: 10–12 days
Young in nest: 10–13 days
No. broods: 2
Season: Apr–Jul

Seasonality

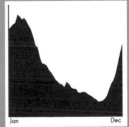

Jan   Dec

Chiffchaff

Summer

Winter

Status

Green listed. Recovering from mid-1970s crash.

Foods

Insects, some fruit in autumn.

Breeding

Clutch size: 4–7
Incubates: c.13 days
Young in nest: c.14 days
No. broods: 1–2
Season: Apr–Aug

Seasonality

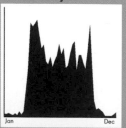

Jan   Dec

The Chiffchaff is a *Phylloscopus* (or leaf) warbler, one of a group of 45 or so species, all of which are small and often similar in colour. While some rural gardens may hold breeding Chiffchaffs, they are only occasional garden visitors, most commonly reported during the autumn. This is the time of year when young birds explore the wider landscape, before beginning their migration through southern Europe and into North Africa. These immature birds sometimes associate with roving flocks of tits. The Chiffchaff is one of the few songbirds with an onomatopoeic name, in this case derived from its 'chiff-chaff' song, familiar to most birdwatchers and often heard throughout spring. The scientific name of '*collybita*' is also derived from the song, coming from the Greek word '*collubistesi*' which means '*money-changer*' – the reference here being to the sound of money being counted.

Over the last 30 years or so, there has been a noticeable increase in the number of Chiffchaffs wintering in Britain, although they are only occasionally seen in gardens. Almost all of the wintering Chiffchaffs remain within the wider countryside feeding on invertebrates. Records often come from sites on the south and southwest coasts, near to water, where there is a better supply of insects through the winter months. It is not known from where these birds originate. Some may breed in Britain and Ireland but others are known to come from farther east and show the characteristics of other races.

Numbers at wintering sites peak in December and then drop-off somewhat before the arrival of the first spring migrants. If the winter weather across southern Europe has been relatively mild then the first migrants may appear in southern England during early March, although it is usually April before they reach northern Scotland. These returning migrants occupy territories in a wide range of woodland habitats, seeking out areas with some tall trees to use as songposts, together with suitable ground cover in which to nest. Chiffchaffs usually build a nest within about 1m of the ground, nesting on the ground less frequently than the Willow Warbler. The Chiffchaff is very similar in appearance to the Willow Warbler and the two species often pose identification problems (see box). Most of the incubation and brooding is done by the female, as is much of the feeding of the developing chicks.

The Chiffchaff appears smaller and dumpier looking in its appearance than the Willow Warnler, with dark legs and rather dull plumage. The Willow Warbler is a larger, bright bird with stronger green tones and typically pale legs. Fortunately, the songs given by the two species are very different and aid identification.

Chiffchiff by Tommy Holden

This is our smallest bird. It weighs 5g and is 9cm in length, making it about 30% smaller than a Blue Tit and 55% lighter. What makes the Goldcrest remarkable is that while some are migrants, undertaking long sea crossings to avoid the cold winters of northern regions, others remain in areas where darkness can last for 18 hours and temperatures fall to −25°C. Under such conditions, Goldcrests, huddling together for warmth, may still burn off 20% of their body weight overnight.

Goldcrests are birds of coniferous woodland, where their thin bills, agility and small size enable them to feed on the insects found at the very ends of branches, places where larger birds cannot forage. Some pairs breed in larger gardens where mature conifers are present. However, outside of the breeding season they range more widely and often feature in gardens, where they can occasionally be seen feeding at bird tables on soft fat and bread. The Garden BirdWatch reporting rate is quite low (at about 3%) for much of the year but does peak at 9% in both spring and autumn (when migrants may be passing through the country). One other reason for the low reporting rate is that this species can be very difficult to spot. Its song and call note are very high pitched and often go unnoticed.

Goldcrests are known to be vulnerable to periods of severe winter weather. Their small size means that they chill more quickly than larger birds and they cannot store as much fat. To overcome this problem, they regularly roost together to conserve energy. They also use energy-saving behaviours during the breeding season. The nest is well insulated with a layer of feathers and the chicks minimise heat loss by burrowing down into the lower part of the nest once they have been fed. Despite having a large brood, the female will start a second clutch in another nest while her mate continues to feed the first brood. The effects of cold winters on our breeding population can be seen from BTO data gathered through the Common Birds Census, most notably following the 1962/63 winter. Goldcrests may be short-lived birds, with a high turnover of individuals, but they are able to rear a good number of young each year, if conditions are favourable, and this enables their populations to recover surprisingly quickly from the effects of cold winters.

Summer

Winter

Status

Amber listed. Long-term trend appears stable.

Foods

Insects, spiders, fat and small peanut fragments.

Breeding

Clutch size: 7–8
Incubates: c.16 days
Young in nest: 18–20 days
No. broods: 2
Season: Apr–Aug

Seasonality

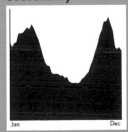

Jan   Dec

Goldcrests look busy as they forage on the outer branches of conifers, and often flick their wings as they move. The central crown stripe is orange-yellow in the male and lemon-yellow in the female. In both sexes this is flanked by lines of black. The male uses these markings to good effect during courtship, puffing out his feathers to display the orange crown to his mate.

Goldcrest by Tommy Holden

Spotted Flycatcher

Summer

Winter

Status

Red listed.
Probably decreasing in gardens.

Foods

Insects, caught in flight, some fruit taken.

Breeding

Clutch size: 4–5
Incubates: 12–14days
Young in nest: 12–15 days
No. broods: 1–2
Season: May–Aug

Seasonality

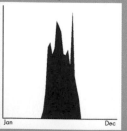

Jan   Dec

The Spotted Flycatcher is one of the last summer migrants to reach us, typically arriving from the middle of May. Despite this late arrival, they may still manage to rear two broods of young before departing in late August. Spotted Flycatchers may be able to do this because they lay fewer eggs in their second clutch and because some of the young from the first clutch help to feed their younger siblings.

Spotted Flycatchers are birds of woodland edge but are also found nesting in rural and suburban gardens. Garden nests are usually built against a wall, on a ledge or behind climbing plants, hence the local name of 'wall bird' used in some parts of England. The nest may be built on top of the old nest of a thrush or Swallow and tends to be reasonably well-hidden. The bird itself is rather unobtrusive, drab in colour, with a soft squeaky song. However, they are often easy to spot because of their tendency to perch on an exposed post or branch, from which they make a darting flight to grab passing insects. Large flying insects are the preferred prey, particularly large flies, but the adults will take smaller insects from leaves and branches if the weather is cool and flying insects are unavailable. Because smaller insects tend to be eaten directly rather than being fed to the chicks, many Spotted Flycatcher nests will fail if the weather remains poor for a week or more. In summers with better weather, the birds are able to breed earlier and raise more chicks. When the female is forming her eggs she will often start to feed on woodlice and snails, both of which are rich in the calcium needed to form eggshells. The male will often support her at this stage by bringing extra food.

Our Spotted Flycatchers migrate south through western France and Iberia to winter in Africa. Ringing research shows that some of these winter in Western Africa, south of the Sahara but others may move farther south across the Equator to winter in South Africa. Difficulties encountered when migrating through the very dry Sahel region of Africa may have contributed to the 85% decline in Spotted Flycatcher numbers breeding in Britain since 1974. Recent BTO research suggests that other factors might also be involved, most notably a decline in the survival rates of young Spotted Flycatchers during their first year of life, maybe even during the first few weeks after leaving their nests.

Young Spotted Flycatchers (right) live up to their name, being much more heavily spotted than their parents (left). Spotted Flycatchers have a broad bill which helps them catch flies. They readily take to open-fronted nestboxes.

Spotted Flycatchers by Tommy Holden

Despite its name, the Long-tailed Tit is only distantly related to the familiar Blue and Great Tits with which it often associates. It does not nest in a cavity but instead constructs a delicate domed nest, spherical in shape and placed either low down in dense bushes or high up in the fork of a tree. Choosing a thorny site seems to offer some protection from the very high levels of nest predation that these birds suffer, often by Jays or Magpies. Nest building often starts early in March and may take several weeks to complete, hardly surprising given that the nest is finely constructed using moss, lichen (for camouflage), spiders' webs and up to 2,000 feathers. Adults whose own breeding attempts have failed may act as helpers at the nests of their relatives.

The behaviour of this species has been very well-studied and we now understand the complex interactions that take place between the various members of the small parties that may gather together in the winter. These often include the parents and young from several nests, together with adult birds that had failed to rear chicks during the breeding season. Many of the birds in these parties will be related and together they defend a winter feeding territory. They also roost communally, a trait which makes a very important contribution to being able to survive the cold winter nights. Long-tailed Tits do not roost in holes, but huddle close together, often in a line along a branch in the middle of a bush. Towards the end of the winter, unpaired females leave the group and join a neighbouring party. The remaining pairs start to build nests within their winter range, continuing to roost communally until the dome of the nest is complete.

Cold winters can reduce the breeding population by up to 80% but in recent years numbers have been increasing. Another recent feature has been the increased use of gardens. Garden BirdWatchers have noticed these birds adapting their behaviour to begin feeding from peanut feeders. Historically, Long-tailed Tits have remained more strongly insectivorous than other tits, although there are also records of them feeding on fat, small seeds, bread and cheese crumbs. These are taken from hanging feeders, bird tables and from the ground. It appears that, once one individual within a group learns to exploit a new food source, the other members soon adopt the behaviour. This is another clear benefit of group living.

Long-tailed Tits have small black, white and pink bodies and a long tail. Young birds are duller in colour than their parents and lack the pink colouring completely. Because the young moult their feathers soon after leaving the nest, they soon look identical to their parents.

Long-tailed Tit by Tommy Holden

Summer

Winter

Status

Green listed.
Increasing in gardens.

Foods

Insects, plant material, peanuts and fat.

Breeding

Clutch size: 7–12
Incubates: 14–18 days
Young in nest: 15–16 days
No. broods: 1
Season: Mar–Jun

Seasonality

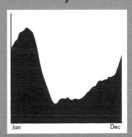

Jan   Dec

Coal Tit

Coal Tit
by Tommy Holden

The Coal Tit is the smallest member of the 'true' tits to be found in Britain & Ireland. As a consequence it comes at the bottom of the pecking order and so has to use those nest sites and feeding locations that the more dominant species find less appealing. This is why Coal Tits can often be found using smaller cavities, positioned closer to the ground, than those favoured by Blue and Great Tits. Small size enables this agile species to feed in the upper parts of trees, typically at the outer end of branches, where larger birds cannot forage.

Competition with the other tit species may also be the reason why Coal Tits prefer coniferous woodland to the broad-leaved habitats more usually associated with this group of birds. Coal Tits can be very common within coniferous woodland and have evolved a narrow bill, ideal for gleaning food from between pine needles. Interestingly, British Coal Tits more regularly use broad-leaved woodland than their continental cousins and have slightly larger bills than their counterparts. In Ireland, where there are fewer conifers, Coal Tit bills are even larger. However. Coal Tits within Britain and Ireland still appear to do best where there are conifers (especially yew), and even just a few conifers in a suburban garden may be sufficient to encourage a pair to set up home.

During most winters, when insect food is in short supply, Coal Tits switch to taking tree seeds, notably beech mast. The availability of beech mast (and other seeds) has been shown by the BTO's David Glue to determine the degree to which Coal Tits move into gardens during the winter months. When there is little beech mast available in the wider countryside, more Coal Tits move into gardens to feed on peanuts and black sunflower seed. Coal Tits are well-known hoarders of food, making repeat visits to a feeder to carry away nuts or seeds for storage in a hidden cache. The storage of food in this manner is really an insurance policy, bracing the bird against the risk of food shortage later in the winter. For a small bird that cannot carry large reserves of fat, this is a good idea and an excellent survival strategy. In Europe, Coal Tits may make very long distance movements during the winter in search of food. Some of these movements bring birds across the English Channel and into the southern counties of England. We know this from recoveries here of birds ringed in Germany and the Netherlands.

Although they will readily take to nestboxes, Coal Tits are sometimes ousted by the other tits, so to get them breeding in a box in your garden you either need to provide lots of boxes or place a box within a conifer and low to the ground. Using a box with a very small aperture (about 25mm) is another option or you could try using a narrow vertical slit rather than a round hole. Coal Tits nest slightly earlier than Blue Tits and laying usually begins in early-April in southern Britain (later further north). The nest is constructed of moss and lined with fur or hair, occasionally with a small number of feathers.

Coal Tits have distinctive features, easy to recognise if you can get a good view of the head. The Coal Tit has a black cap, white cheeks and a large rectangular white patch on the nape of its neck, a feature not shared by any other European tit.

*Coal Tit
by Tommy Holden*

Competition and dominance in tits

The different tit species reduce competition with each other in several ways: (1) by feeding in different habitats, (2) by feeding at different heights above the ground, (3) by feeding in different parts of a tree and (4) by feeding on different items. However, there is still a dominance hierarchy with the largest species coming at the top of the pecking order (see below).

Great Tit
Weight: 14–22g
Habitat: Broadleaf woodland
Feeds: On ground and in lower branches

Blue Tit
Weight: 9.5–12.5g
Habitat: Broadleaf woodland
Feeds: High in tree canopy

Willow Tit
Weight: 10–14g
Habitat: Broadleaf/conifer woodland
Feeds: Low down but rarely on the ground

Marsh Tit
Weight: 10-13g
Habitat: Broadleaf woodland
Feeds: On ground and in lower branches

Crested Tit
Weight: 10–13g
Habitat: Conifer woodland in Scottish Highlands
Feeds: In canopy but also on ground in summer

Coal Tit
Weight: 8–10g
Habitat: Conifer/broadleaf woodland
Feeds: In canopy at end of brances

Long-tailed Tit
Weight: 7–10g
Habitat: Broadleaf woodland
Feeds: High in tree canopy

Competition and dominance photographs by Tommy Holden, Dick Jeeves and G Olioso

Status
Green listed.
Population stable.

Foods
Insects, spiders and seeds, especially spruce.

Breeding
Clutch size: 7–11
Incubates: 13–14 days
Young in nest: 16–17 days
No. broods: 1(2)
Season: Mar–Jul

Seasonality

Great Tit

Arguably the most handsome of our tit species, the Great Tit, is also the largest. This, coupled with its habit of feeding on the ground, make the Great Tit a very adaptable species and one that can be found across a wide range of woodland and semi-open habitats (Great Tits even inhabit mangrove forests in Malaysia). As such, its bold plumage and loud, ringing song are familiar to most, if not all, garden birdwatchers. Great Tits also show a willingness to utilise nest boxes, maybe because natural cavities with a large enough entrance hole are hard to find. The most familiar of the various calls that Great Tits are known to make is the '*teacher teacher*' call, often heard from late winter. Male Great Tits often develop a number of variations on the basic song but these have to be acquired, meaning that older birds are more diverse in their repertoire than young ones – one older male was found to use some 40 different songs. The amount of time spent singing declines once nesting starts (usually in April) and the female begins incubation.

Eggs are laid at a rate of about one a day and are similar in appearance to those laid by other tits, though larger in size. They are glossy white with a variable degree of red-brown spotting concentrated at the blunt end. The female roosts in the nesting cavity once the first egg has been laid but, even though she is in contact with them, she is not generating enough heat to start the incubation process. This only begins once all the eggs have been laid. The heat needed to allow the eggs to develop comes from the female through her brood patch. This is an area of bare skin that develops just prior to incubation, rich in blood vessels and hot to the touch. The female is able to maintain the surface temperature of the eggs at about 35.4°C by altering the amount of time she spends incubating them. Typically, this involves 30 minutes of incubation followed by a 10 minute break.

When they emerge from the eggs, each chick weighs just over a gramme and, over the next two weeks or so, will dramatically increase in weight to some 15 times that at hatching. How well the developing chick does is dependent upon food availability, weather conditions and competition from other species (like Blue Tit and various warblers) also feeding their young on caterpillars. Great Tits raised in garden nest boxes are smaller than those in woodland, reflecting the reduced availability of caterpillars in human landscapes. Once the chicks leave the nest, they are reliant on their parents for another couple of weeks. During this period the family party will travel some distance to find food and often features at bird tables, where the food we provide may be very important, since starvation is known to be a major cause of death.

Great Tits use their feet to hold large food items, like beech mast and acorns, while hammering

Great Tit by
George Higginbotham

these seeds open with their bill. A similar approach is used to kill caterpillars, a very important prey during the late spring and summer months. Dr Andy Gosler, who has studied Great Tits for many years, once calculated that the effort of feeding chicks was equivalent to a human parent bringing home over 100kg of shopping every day for three weeks! Of course, caterpillars are only available in quantity for a short period and so, as summer moves into autumn, Great Tits begin to take more tree seeds. During the winter months, as seed supplies begin to run low, woodland populations of Great Tits become more mobile and often visit gardens to feed on the food we provide. One finding from recent research is that, as adult Great Tits switch from feeding on seeds in winter to feeding on caterpillars in spring, their bills become longer and less deep. Such changes are very small but appear to be enough to make the bill better suited to a diet of invertebrates – a short, robust bill being better for dealing with nuts and seeds.

Status signals

The black stripe running down the breast plays an important role in Great Tit behaviour, acting as a badge denoting the status of the individual. In females, the stripe peters out about halfway down the belly, while in males it continues down between the legs and is both broader and bolder than in the female. There is less variation between members of the same sex but these subtle differences appear to be enough to show the status of the bird; those with bolder stripes being the more dominant. This 'badge' is shown-off most effectively when birds adopt a head-up display that serves to exaggerate the size of the stripe.

It makes sense for birds to have some way of displaying their status to other individuals, since it helps to avoid unnecessary fights. The social system in Great Tits gives rise to a dominance hierachy and it is the younger (and less dominant) individuals that are forced to feed on less profitable or higher risk feeders. Research has shown that dominant Great Tits choose feeders closest to cover, while younger birds feed at more exposed feeders, where the risk from Sparrowhawks is greater.

Many other garden birds, e.g. House Sparrow, also have dominance hierarchies, often accompanied by some 'badge' used to denote status.

Male Great Tit by Tommy Holden

Status
Green listed. Stable in gardens.

Foods
Insects, seeds, fruit, peanuts and sunflower hearts.

Breeding
Clutch size: 5–12
Incubates: 12–16 days
Young in nest: 18–24 days
No. broods: 1 (2)
Season: Mar-Jul

Seasonality

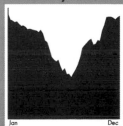

Jan   Dec

Magpie

The Magpie is a bold and conspicuous garden visitor. The striking black and white plumage, together with the harsh chattering 'cha-cha-cha-cha' call, should be familiar to most. Over the last 50 or so years, Magpies have increasingly colonised suburban and urban habitats, making use of the food we provide. This increase in urban and suburban populations ties in with an increase in the Magpie population across most habitats, following a decline in the amount of persecution taking place within the wider countryside. The distribution of breeding Magpies extends right across England, Wales and Ireland. However, the species is more localised within Scotland, being absent from most upland areas as well as from large parts of the Borders. Magpies are sedentary in nature, rarely making long-distance movements and seemingly reluctant to cross large stretches of water.

Magpies obviously find the urban environment an ideal one in which to live. The abundance of food, together with lower levels of persecution, has resulted in breeding densities higher than those seen in farmland habitats. The benefits of living in association with Man, can be seen by the establishment of Magpie populations in the middle of the treeless tundra regions of Russia, where the birds nest on the ground or on buildings, alongside newly established human settlements.

Much of the success of the Magpie comes from the catholic diet and the adaptability that this species shares with other corvids. Various invertebrates, especially insects, form the bulk of the diet, but fruit, grain, berries, carrion and small mammals are also taken. The eggs and young of other birds form part of the diet during the breeding season. One of the most interesting aspects of Magpie feeding behaviour is that of food hoarding, a habit shared with other species like Coal Tit, Jay and Nuthatch. In the case of the Magpie, the caching of food items is of a more short-term nature, with perishable items often recovered and eaten within a few days of being stored. Items are typically deposited in a hole in the ground, dug using the bill, and into which food is regurgitated from a small pouch under the tongue.

The nest is often quite obvious, large in size and placed in the fork of a tree or large shrub. The fact that nest building is a noisy affair, with both birds of a pair chattering, further adds to the ease with which nests can be found. Nest building may begin as early as February but eggs are not normally laid until April. Research carried out in Sheffield has shown that older birds are more likely to finish the nest off with a dome than those birds building a nest for the first time. Inside, the nest is held together with a layer of mud and an inner layer of grass. The image of a Magpie hoarding jewellery or other shiny objects in the nest (or elsewhere) is something of a myth and there is no evidence whatsoever that wild Magpies hoard anything other than food!

Female Magpies begin to incubate their eggs before they have completed laying the entire clutch. This results in

Magpie
by Mike Weston

some eggs hatching earlier than others, a process known as asynchronous hatching, and explains the presence of 'runt' chicks within the brood. It is these small chicks that will die if there is insufficient food available for all the youngsters in a nest. Asynchronous hatching is a survival strategy, helping to ensure that at least

Magpie by Tommy Holden

some chicks survive, even if food conditions are poor. Perhaps surprisingly, only about 50% of the breeding Magpies within an area manage to rear any chicks from their nest, resulting in an average production of just one or two chicks per pair per year. In fact, researchers working in Sheffield found that nearly half of the Magpies in their study population failed to produce any descendents during their lifetimes.

Immature birds gather in non-breeding, non-territory-holding flocks, giving rise to one of the most interesting aspects of Magpie social behaviour, known as ceremonial gatherings. These begin when small groups of immatures target the territory of an established pair. Such incursions elicit a noisy response from the territory owners who chase and attack the intruders, rapidly attracting onlookers in the form of neighbouring pairs and other individuals. These intrusions usually last for a few minutes but they can last for much longer before the birds move on to try their luck elsewhere. The same group of intruders may return to a territory over a period of days, in an attempt to take over part of the territory. Since there is a dominance hierarchy within these groups, it seems likely that it will be the dominant male and his mate which seize the annexed ground if the incursion is successful.

Magpies and songbirds

The perceived 'problem' of Magpie predation on songbirds has its roots in the fact that, while Magpie populations have been recovering from former levels of persecution, the populations of songbirds have declined. Alongside this, instances of Magpie predation of eggs and chicks have tended to elicit a strong emotional response from observers because the conspicuous act of predation is often bloody and associated with a

great deal of commotion. Such a response to nature "red in tooth and claw" is perhaps understandable but the accusations made against the Magpie, suggesting it is the cause of widespread population declines, are unsupported by scientific evidence.

Magpie by Tommy Holden

Status
Green listed.
Now stable following period of recovery.

Foods
Invertebrates, seeds, fruit, carrion, scraps and eggs.

Breeding
Clutch size: 5–7
Incubates: 17–18 days
Young in nest: 22–27 days
No. broods: 1
Season: Mar–Jun

Seasonality

Jan   Dec

Jay

Status

Green listed. Long-term trend appears stable.

Foods

Invertebrates, fruit, seeds, small birds and eggs.

Breeding

Clutch size: 5–6

Incubates: c.16 days

Young in nest: c.20 days

No. broods: 1

Season: Apr–Jul

Seasonality

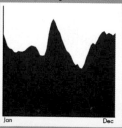

Jan   Dec

Jays are usually wary birds within the woodland habitats they favour. In gardens they can become surprisingly approachable, most probably because this is a habitat within which they are rarely persecuted. The Jay is one of just 13 species that can be legally controlled throughout the year, reflecting their habit of taking the young and eggs of various gamebirds. However, it is tree seeds (especially acorns) on which they specialise, often hoarding huge numbers throughout the autumn to be eaten later in the year. Persecution has helped to shape the distribution of the Jay throughout Britain and Ireland, and has also played a part in setting population levels. The Jay is now more widely distributed than it was in the 19th Century and is only really absent from upland areas and the fens.

Jays are at their most conspicuous during the autumn, when they often travel some distance to find abundant supplies of acorns. Birds will typically collect and hold 3–4 acorns in their adapted gullet (plus one in their bill) before returning to their territories, where the acorns will be stored in the ground. You may be fortunate enough to witness a Jay hoarding acorns in your lawn. First, the bird makes a hole in the ground at a 45-degree angle using its bill. One or two acorns are then deposited in the hole before the bird uses sideways movements of its bill to cover its store. It has been estimated that a single Jay may hoard up to 3,000 acorns during a month and this makes its ability to relocate these stores all the more amazing. Sometimes, especially during the summer, Jays can use the presence of a newly germinated oak sapling to reveal the presence of a hidden acorn attached to its base. When it comes to eating an acorn, a Jay will grasp it in both feet, holding it against the perch, before prising off bits of the shell to make a hole through which it can feed on what is inside. Acorns can be an unpredictable food source and there are years when very few acorns are produced. During such years, substantial numbers of Jays from northern and eastern Europe arrive in Britain in search of food.

Jays do not usually gather together in large flocks. The small groups that may form during spring are thought to be unpaired birds looking for partners. Even established pairs tend to spend much of their time apart, seemingly avoiding close contact except when defending their territory or mating.

Results from both the Garden Bird Feeding Survey and Garden BirdWatch illustrate the use that Jays can make of gardens. In many cases they visit gardens early in the morning to take peanuts, scraps and even marmalade on toast. Some enterprising individuals have learned to up-end hanging peanut feeders in order to empty the contents.

Jay by Mike Weston

Although Jackdaws occur in greatest numbers in areas of mixed farming and pasture, well-stocked with cattle and sheep, they are equally at home in large gardens, where they will often nest in chimneys, tree cavities or even nestboxes. Jackdaws are gregarious birds, nesting colonially and gathering together with other crows in large winter roosts. However, the basic unit of Jackdaw society is the pair and individual birds are extremely faithful to their mates. The pair bond is so strong that birds will remain together even when they have been unsuccessful in their breeding attempts over several seasons. One of the reasons suggested for the presence of such a strong pair bond is that the birds have to put in a huge amount of effort early in the breeding season in order to find enough food for their developing chicks. Jackdaw eggs hatch asynchronously (incubation begins before all the eggs have been laid) and this means that the young differ in age. The oldest chicks can hold their gaping mouths higher than their siblings and so get the lion's share of the food being delivered to the nest. It is only during those years when food is really abundant that the parents manage to rear all the chicks that hatch.

Although Jackdaws are catholic in their diet, they concentrate on invertebrates during the breeding season, taking the larvae of moths and flies from the surface of the ground. Bird tables are probably more frequently visited than many people imagine, Jackdaws often arriving very early in the morning to take whatever is available, especially during early summer.

Most nests are in cavities (including chimneys) and the male will drop sticks into the hole until some begin to catch, allowing a platform to be constructed. Once this has been completed, the female will create a bowl and add a lining, often of wool. Prior to nest building, the pair will often perch at the entrance, a clear signal that the site will be used in the weeks ahead. Once the eggs hatch, the female will remain with the chicks over the first 10–12 days, while the male brings food for both her and the chicks. At this stage, the female may leave the nest for brief periods, to preen and exercise, leaving the male to guard the young. The chicks remain in the nest for almost five weeks and, even once they have fledged, the adults still have to provide food for them for several more weeks.

Summer

Winter

Status

Green listed. Increasing in rural gardens.

Foods

Invertebrates, seeds, scraps, carrion and fruit.

Breeding

Clutch size: 4–6
Incubates: 17–18 days
Young in nest: 30–35 days
No. broods: 1
Season: Apr–Jun

Seasonality

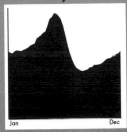

Jan   Dec

The Jackdaw is the smallest of our black crows, being about two–thirds of the size of a Rook or Carrion Crow. Young Jackdaws lack the distinctive grey colour to the nape and sides of the head of the adult but do have wonderful blue-grey eyes. As the chicks get older, the eye changes colour, becoming brown in their first winter and pearly white when they attain the adult breeding plumage.

Jackdaw by Tommy Holden

Rook

Status

Green Listed.
Shallow long-term increase.

Foods

Earthworms and beetles,
plant material and carrion.

Breeding

Clutch size: 4–6
Incubates: 16–19 days
Young in nest: 29–30 days
No. broods: 1
Season: Mar–Jun

Seasonality

Jan   Dec

Rooks are closely associated with agricultural land below 300m and it is not surprising that the majority of Garden BirdWatch records come from large rural gardens. However, in some parts of their range, Rooks will readily enter the outer suburbs of large towns in search of food or nesting opportunities. The colonial nests made by Rooks, placed high in mature trees, are familiar to most as 'rookeries'. These are noisy affairs, especially during the early part of the breeding season, when pairs reclaim nests used the previous year. Pairs can remain together for several years, if successful in their breeding attempts, and roost together even when they join the huge winter roosts. Such communal roosts often contain many thousands of individuals from different rookeries, including some that may have travelled up to 20km. One roost in Scotland was estimated to contain some 65,000 birds – a staggering figure. In order to reach the roosts, small groups of Rooks will travel along well-defined lines of flight, arriving close to the roost before dark and joining other birds that have already ceased feeding and are preening or generally loafing around. As it gets dark, the birds move into the trees that form the roost site.

Rooks are less catholic in their diet than the other large crows and specialise on soil-living invertebrates, particularly earthworms, and cereal grain. Birds feed by probing and digging with their long, pointed bills. Feeding Rooks have a confident upright stance as they walk about in search of suitable prey.

Recent changes in farming methods have caused problems for Rooks and have brought them into conflict with farmers. Changes in cropping practices mean that germinating cereal crops are now available to Rooks at the very time of year when other foods are difficult to find. Being adaptable birds, and unlikely to miss a free lunch, the Rooks can inflict localised, but heavy damage, to these crops. In response, some landowners shoot young Rooks on the nest in an attempt to control the population. Controlling a population by removing a proportion of the young birds is often unsuccessful. Many young birds would die anyway and the remaining birds end up with with a greater share of the available resources, which means that they are more likely to survive than they would otherwise.

The persecution of Rooks in the wider countryside has made them wary of associating with Man. In some urban areas, or in large rural gardens where they are regularly fed, they may become remarkably confiding and approachable, to the extent where they become a nuisance, monopolizing feeding stations. A gathering of Rooks is commonly known as a 'parliament', quite a fitting description.

Rook by George Higginbotham

Carrion Crows are found across England, Wales and into Scotland, but are rare in Ireland. They occupy a wide range of habitats, including open woodland, farmland, coastal margins and, increasingly, have spread into urban areas. Hooded Crows occur in northwest Scotland, Ireland and on the Isle of Man. Hooded Crows appear to be birds of poorer quality land, something that is supported by their displacement from lowland agricultural land in the Scottish lowlands during the 20th Century by Carrion Crows. Traditionally, the Carrion and Hooded Crow have been regarded as being two races of the same species, since they interbreed freely and produce fertile offspring. However, hybrids produced from matings between birds of the two forms are very unsuccessful, resulting in a striking lack of mixed pairs. A very narrow 'hybrid zone', where intermediate forms occur, is a consequence of this, reducing the amount of gene flow. Other research has highlighted subtle differences in the vocalisations made by the two forms and in habitat use. Taken together, these findings have enabled taxonomists to recommend that the two forms be treated as separate species on the British List. Within Garden BirdWatch, the two species have been recorded under Carrion Crow.

Unlike Rooks and Jackdaws, these crows are solitary nesters, defending large territories around the nest site for much of the year. The nest is usually built high in a tree but may be on a cliff face, building or other structure. Territory boundaries are less aggressively defended against neighbouring pairs than against other birds and this allows for mutual defence against intruders. Flocks usually consist of immature birds and birds of breeding age lacking a territory. Communal roosts form in the winter, largely involving birds from these floating flocks, and sometimes involving other species like Rook and Jackdaw.

The highly adaptable nature of these crows has brought them into conflict with Man. Game-keepers often control crows because they will take eggs and young chicks. Similarly, sheep farmers have controlled them because they scavenge carrion and have been blamed for killing young lambs. Insects are the staple diet in summer, supplemented by carrion and other scavenged food, while in winter grain is important. Individuals have also been recorded opening milk bottle tops to get at the cream and taking shellfish on the seashore.

The Carrion Crow has a heavier black bill than the Rook and lacks the shaggy thighs. It also has a flatter crown to the head. Both Rook and Carrion Crow are noticeably smaller than the Raven. The Hooded Crow has a black head, wings and tail and a grey body. The typical call of these crows is a resonant 'kraa', stronger than the rather flat call of the Rook. Carrion and Hooded Crows are usually seen in pairs or small groups.

Carrion Crow by Tommy Holden

Summer

Winter

Status
Green list. The Carrion Crow has increased steadily since the 1960s.

Foods
Invertebrates, cereal grain, eggs, carrion and scraps.

Breeding
Clutch size: 4–6
Incubates: c.19 days
Young in nest: 26–35 days
No. broods: 1
Season: Mar–Jul

Seasonality

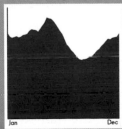

Jan   Dec

Starling

*Starlings
by Mike Weston*

The Starling has gained the somewhat unfair reputation of being an argumentative and greedy bird. As such, many garden birdwatchers regard the Starling as being more of a pest than a welcome visitor to garden feeding stations. In fact, the Starling is well adapted to group living and has some fascinating aspects to its ecology and behaviour. Starlings have two main requirements in the breeding season: a suitable hole in which to nest and nearby grassland where they can feed. Such requirements are met in many habitats, including urban ones, so the Starling has become an abundant species across most of Britain and Ireland. It may seem surprising, therefore, that just over 150 years ago the Starling was a scarce bird.

A wide range of cavities may be used for nesting, including those under the eaves of houses, although the increased use of uPVC bargeboards has resulted in the loss of many urban nesting opportunities. Starlings have been recorded taking over the nests of House Sparrows, Swifts and even Sand Martins, ejecting the owners and setting up home themselves. Mature males may establish nesting territories in January, defending a small area around the nest hole and advertising for a mate. Many males will grab several holes and try to attract a mate to each one but competition for nest sites usually means that a male will be unable to defend all the holes he initially claims. However, it is not unusual for a male to mate with more than one female having successfully defended multiple nest sites. Females may also display some opportunistic behaviour when it comes to breeding. It is quite common for a female Starling to deposit one of her eggs in another female's nest. This is known as brood parasitism, a practice which is quite rare in birds (occurring in just 1% of species). On occasion, to reduce the chances of her egg being spotted in another female's clutch, a female will remove an egg after she has deposited her own so that the numbers still add up. It is these eggs that may sometimes be found on the ground.

During the breeding season, Starlings feed primarily on invertebrates, especially leatherjackets taken from short grassland. Small feeding flocks, running or walking across lawns, are a familiar sight to many at this time of the year. During the late summer and autumn, the amount of plant material taken increases, reflecting food availability. This seasonal shift in diet is matched by a change in the length of the Starling's intestine, which gets longer to cope with a diet that is composed largely of plant material. Plant material is more difficult to digest than animal material and a longer intestine increases the amount of nutrients that the body can absorb. Other adaptations shown by the Starling and related to feeding can be seen in the structure of the Starling's head. Modifications to the skull, and the musculature around it, allow the Starling to push its bill into the soil and then open it to create a hole. As the bill opens, the eyes rotate forwards to give the bird binocular vision, something that is useful in spotting prey within reach of the bill.

There are two distinct components to our Starling population: a resident population, that remains within Britain and Ireland throughout the year, plus a huge wintering population of birds that arrive from breeding grounds elsewhere in Europe. The presence

Juvenile Starling by Mike Weston

of these two populations can be see in the Garden BirdWatch reporting rate for this species. The reporting rate increases dramatically in the winter months, coinciding with the influx of migrants, and there are pronounced peaks throughout the winter associated with cold weather movements of immigrants into gardens.

It is during October and November that most of the winter visitors arrive, although individuals from different European breeding populations migrate at different times and use a number of different routes to reach our shores. Most of the Starlings breeding in western Europe migrate along a flyway that runs through northern Germany and the Low Countries. Birds from the Netherlands are the first to arrive, followed later by individuals from breeding populations in Scandinavia and Germany. The last birds to arrive come from Poland and Russia. During the winter months, vast roosting flocks may gather, performing amazing aerobatic displays before dropping into favoured roost sites (see pages 36–37). These large flocks can cause problems, contaminating buildings and causing public nuisance, prompting some councils to scare roosting birds away.

Status
Red listed. Widespread decline in numbers.

Foods
Insects, plant material, grain, scraps and fat.

Breeding
Clutch size: 4–7
Incubates: 12–14 days
Young in nest: 20–22 days
No. broods: 1 (2)
Season: Mar–Jul

Seasonality

Jan   Dec

Stretching

Wing stretching is a behaviour that is common to all birds and it can often be seen in gardens. Small birds, like the Starling, typically stretch one wing downwards, together with the corresponding leg. This movement is often accompanied by the fanning out of the tail. In larger birds, notably

some waders, both wings are stretched upwards, to the extent that they almost touch, and it is thought that this might have some social significance. Wing stretching is one of a number of comfort behaviours which, along with others like grooming, help to keep the bird in good condition, in this case reducing the risk of muscle strain.

Starling by Mike Weston

Summer

Winter

The House Sparrow has been the source of much concern in recent years. The dramatic population declines that have been revealed by BTO monitoring programmes, like the Garden Bird Feeding Survey and the Common Birds Census, have prompted research to establish why such a familiar species, so strongly associated with Man, is in difficulty. The House Sparrow breeding population is thought to number between six and seven million pairs, having fallen from around 12 million pairs during the 1970s. Just under two-thirds of these pairs occur in towns and villages, including about two million pairs in suburban habitats, mostly in southern, eastern and central England. Results from the Garden Bird Feeding Survey show that the decline began in the mid–1980s in rural gardens and slightly later in suburban gardens, both populations following the pattern of an earlier decline within farmland habitats. It has long been thought that the decline has not been uniform across the whole of Britain and Ireland, and the Garden BirdWatch data support this. Even during the relatively short period over which the Garden BirdWatch project has been running, the rate of decline in London and southeast England has been far more pronounced than in Scotland or Wales.

There is evidence to suggest that the decline has been most acute in urban and rural areas and less pronounced in suburban habitats. This supports the theory of some Dutch scientists, who believe that suburban gardens are the preferred habitat of House Sparrows and act as source populations for poorer quality habitats in rural and urban areas. This is something that the Garden BirdWatch House Sparrow Project is examining in greater detail.

Traditionally, there was a mid-winter peak in the use that House Sparrows made of garden feeding stations, the timing of which was earlier in pastoral landscapes than in arable ones, presumably reflecting the higher abundance of grain and weed seeds in arable fields. This mid-winter peak has effectively disappeared, with peak House Sparrow numbers now occurring during October. Over the course of the last thirty years, the peak has gradually crept back earlier and earlier in the year, suggesting that food resources in the wider countryside have been depleted more quickly as time has gone on, a sure sign of a problem for the House Sparrow.

The underlying causes of the declines seen across rural, suburban and urban habitats may well be different, since House Sparrows rarely move very far. Within rural areas, changes in farming practices, notably the loss of overwinter stubbles and suitable nest sites, may have

Male (top) and female (bottom) House Sparrows by John Harding

driven the decline. In urban and suburban habitats a wider range of factors may be implicated. These include: (1) loss of nest sites as new designs of roof tile and barge board restrict access to traditional nesting sites, (2) increased levels of predation from Sparrowhawks and domestic cats – one study in a Bedfordshire village showed that cats were responsible for 30% of the House Sparrow mortality, (3) increased competition from increasing populations of Feral Pigeons, Collared Doves and Woodpigeons, (4) a decline in sources of weed seeds due to the loss of over-grown, unused, city sites, (5) a decline in availability of those insect species important in chick diet because of increased pesticide use in gardens, (6) increased levels of pollution, (7) changes in the suitability of foods provided at garden feeding stations, (8) loss of suitable roosting sites and (9) increased levels of disease transmission. Work being carried out as part of the Garden BirdWatch House Sparrow Project is looking at each of these factors.

Male House Sparrow and young by Tommy Holden.

Even with the decline, the House Sparrow remains a familiar visitor to many garden feeding stations. The communal nature of the House Sparrow is at its most obvious during the winter, when small flocks often gather in trees or bushes and 'chatter' between bouts of feeding. House Sparrows are most attracted to hanging seed and peanut feeders which have plenty of space for several birds to feed at once, and within easy reach of cover. House Sparrows are seed-eaters by nature, but within the garden environment, many different kitchen scraps are taken. Winter feeding flocks usually contain birds from several local colonies and it is through these that the young disperse away from the colony in which they were born. Many of the individuals in these flocks will roost together in dense vegetation, although birds that have bred during the previous summer will often roost in the nest site.

House Sparrows establish their nest sites and form pairs early in the season. In addition to nesting in cavities, House Sparrows will also build rather untidy nests within dense vegetation. House Sparrows sometimes take over nests built by House Martins, and have even been recorded living and breeding underground in coal mines. Established birds pair for life and tend to use the same nest site each year. Males will perch above the nest hole and proclaim their ownership. Young birds will attempt to attract a mate once they have found a hole and the females use the black bib of the male as a means of assessing his suitability. Dominant males have larger bibs, so an established older male that has lost its mate will probably secure a new female before a younger, less dominant individual.

Status
Red listed.
Pronounced decline in numbers.

Foods
Seeds, plant material and insects.

Breeding
Clutch size: 3–6
Incubates: 9–18 days
Young in nest: 11–19 days
No. broods: 1–4
Season: Mar–Aug

Seasonality

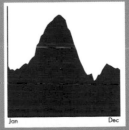

Tree Sparrow

Summer

Winter

Status

Red listed.
Sharp decline in numbers.

Foods

Seeds, plant material
and insects.

Breeding

Clutch size: 4–6
Incubates: 12–14 days
Young in nest: 12–15 days
No. broods: 2 (3)
Season: Apr–Aug

Seasonality

Jan   Dec

The Tree Sparrow is the less-familiar relative of the House Sparrow, traditionally found in farmland and rural gardens around the edges of villages across much of England, Wales and lowland Scotland. In Ireland, the species is largely restricted to coastal localities, though inland colonies have become established in Northern Ireland. Some rural garden birdwatchers will have Tree Sparrows nesting in their gardens, sometimes in cavities in the roof, in thatch or in old tree holes or nestboxes, but others will have them visiting during the winter months, when garden feeding stations may be an important source of food. Curiously, elsewhere in the world Tree Sparrows are urban birds, often living alongside House Sparrows.

The Tree Sparrow population has shown both dramatic increases and decreases over the last hundred years, with a fivefold increase in the 1960s and 1970s followed by an equally large and rapid decline since the 1970s. Information from the BTO's Common Birds Census suggests a decline of 87% between 1972 and 1996 and the species is now Red listed, as a bird of high conservation concern. Tree Sparrows breed in loose colonies of 10–50 pairs which fluctuate dramatically. Some build up over a very short period, remain for a few years and then suddenly disappear. Part of the reason for such changes may be colony structure and the availability of nesting and feeding opportunities. Just over one-third of the birds in a typical colony are adults from the previous year, a further 5% are juveniles born at the colony, while the remainder are juveniles from other colonies. Once established, colonies do not appear to increase in size, the surplus juveniles emigrating to join other colonies. It may be this feature, coupled with the short lifespan of Tree Sparrows, that drives the establishment of new colonies and the loss of old ones.

While insects are included in the diet during the breeding season, and the young are raised entirely on them, Tree Sparrows specialise on the seeds of arable weeds like chickweed. Gardens are more often visited in the winter months, when birds take mixed seed, fat and peanuts, preferably from the ground, but also from bird tables and hanging feeders. Visiting flocks often indulge in social singing, a behaviour that is thought to reinforce the cohesion of the flock.

Breeding Tree Sparrows tend to pair for life, though only a small proportion of individuals survive through to their second breeding season. Males perch at the nest site during spring to proclaim ownership and, if unpaired, to attract a mate. See page 124 for help on identification of this species.

Tree Sparrow by Tommy Holden

Although the Brambling has been recorded breeding in Britain, it is really a winter visitor, often seen in the company of the closely-related Chaffinch. In fact, the Brambling can be considered as being the northern counterpart of the Chaffinch, occupying breeding grounds in the northern forests of Finland, Norway, Sweden and Russia. Being closely related, the two species are similar in appearance, though the Brambling can be distinguished by its white rump, 'tortoiseshell' upperparts and distinct calls (see page 125).

Bramblings leave their breeding grounds in September and move south, gathering in large flocks in areas with a plentiful supply of beech mast and conifer seeds – favoured foods during the autumn and winter. Flocks often remain in these areas either until the supply of beech mast is depleted or is covered with snow, at which stage they move further south. These movements bring Bramblings into Britain and (to a lesser extent) Ireland from mid-October. Unlike most other finches, Bramblings migrate at night and their arrival right along the east coast of Britain suggests that many make a direct crossing of the North Sea from Scandinavia. Because the availability of beech mast can vary dramatically between years and areas, Brambling movements, and the numbers wintering in Britain, can be equally variable. In some winters we may have just 50,000 Bramblings present, in others in excess of two million may winter here. The Garden BirdWatch reporting rate reflects this and also shows the seasonal pattern to the use of gardens. When birds first arrive they are often unobtrusive, feeding on the ground in woodland but, as beech mast becomes harder to find, they begin to exploit the food provided at garden feeding stations. Reporting of Bramblings in gardens begins in October but does not peak until late winter or early spring.

Bramblings prefer to feed on the ground but will use hanging feeders. It is possible to build up the numbers visiting your garden by regular ground feeding with a mix of premium seed and peanut granules. This mix is also well-used by Chaffinches, with which Bramblings often associate, providing an ideal opportunity to practice your identification skills. Like Chaffinches, male Bramblings tend to winter farther north than females, so you may find that your wintering flock may be mainly of birds of one sex.

The stunning breeding plumage of a male Brambling is concealed in winter by fawn edges to many of the feathers (see photo). These wear off quite suddenly in late winter to reveal a shiny black head. For female see page 125.

Brambling by Tommy Holden

Summer

Winter

Status
Green listed. Winter numbers vary with size of beech mast crop.

Foods
Beech mast, other tree seeds and fruit.

Breeding
Clutch size: 5–7
Incubates: c. 14 days
Young in nest: c. 14 days
No. broods: 1
Season: Apr–Jun

Seasonality

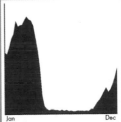

Jan   Dec

Chaffinch

Summer

Winter

The Chaffinch is one of the most abundant and widespread bird species to be found in Britain and Ireland. Although mature deciduous woodland supports the highest densities of breeding Chaffinches, they are equally at home nesting in parks and larger gardens, providing that suitable trees and shrubs are present. This dependence upon tree and shrub cover, for nesting and feeding, is the reason why the Chaffinch is virtually absent during the summer from upland areas, from Shetland and from much of the Outer Hebrides. At this time of the year, the adults take small caterpillars and flies from foliage for their growing chicks, as well as feeding upon other insects taken from the ground. During the autumn and winter, the Chaffinch switches from this diet of insects to feed on a wide range of seeds (more than 100 different types of seed have been recorded in the diet). These seeds are taken from the ground, usually from disturbed soil where they have been brought to the surface. Such ground feeding is a behaviour shared with the closely related Brambling, though the two species avoid direct competition with each other by feeding on different sizes of seeds – the Brambling has a bigger and more robust bill than that of a Chaffinch.

During the breeding season, resident pairs spend most of their time foraging within their breeding territories but they will feed on other open ground, undefended by neighbouring individuals, if feeding conditions are suitable. These resident individuals usually remain within, or close to, their territories during the winter months as well, especially in central and southern Britain. However, in Scotland (and probably in other northern areas) many may leave their territories and form large flocks, to make use of feeding opportunities elsewhere. During the winter, our Chaffinch population is effectively doubled by the arrival of immigrants from continental Europe. Most of these will have come from migratory populations in Norway, Finland and Sweden, involving birds that have travelled through Denmark, northern Germany, Belgium and northeast France to reach Britain by crossing the English Channel. Many of these visitors will remain to winter within southern and central Britain but some, mostly females,

Female Chaffinch by Tommy Holden

subsequently move further north and west to reach Ireland. The largest winter flocks are usually composed of birds of continental origin, while smaller groups of birds are likely to be British and Irish breeders.

One of the most interesting aspects of Chaffinch migration is the differential migration of males and females, with the females migrating further than the males. So extreme is the difference between the two sexes, that females predominate in the wintering population in Ireland, while males dominate populations wintering in Britain, Belgium and The Netherlands. The well-known Swedish naturalist Linnaeus, named the Chaffinch 'coelebs' (Latin for bachelor) because the few Chaffinches remaining to winter in Sweden were nearly always males, seemingly abandoned by their mates. Many of the winter immigrants to Britain and Ireland are still present in early spring, when the resident males have attained their breeding plumage and started to sing for a mate.

Male Chaffinch in breeding plumage by Tommy Holden

Departures of the winter visitors begin in mid-March, the adult males leaving first, followed shortly after by the females and younger birds. The return movements are more direct than those that brought the Chaffinches here in the autumn, with many more birds making a direct crossing of the North Sea, rather than taking a longer route across the English Channel and up through Denmark.

The Chaffinch has evolved into a number of distinct races, the one resident in Britain & Ireland being slightly smaller and more brightly coloured than the continental immigrants. Several islands support their own distinct races, including the Canaries, where the males have a blue-grey back (as opposed to the brown back of our males) that matches the colour on the head. Chaffinches are susceptible to a disease called *Fringilla papillomavirus* and in a recent Dutch study looking at 25,000 Chaffinches, some 1.3% were found to be affected by this wart-forming disease. Cases usually occur in clusters and high proportions of local populations can be affected during outbreaks. The growths occur on the foot or bare part of the leg. They grow slowly and can last for many months, ranging in size from a small nodule up to a deeply-fissured mass that almost engulfs the whole lower leg and foot.

Status

Green listed. Long-term increase in rural gardens.

Foods

Seeds and other plant material. Mainly insects during breeding season.

Breeding

Clutch size: 4–5
Incubates: 11–13 days
Young in nest: 13–14 days
No. broods: 1
Season: Apr–Jul

Seasonality

Male Chaffinch in winter plumage by Tommy Holden

Greenfinch

The Greenfinch is a species that has learnt to utilise gardens and the food provided at feeding stations. Historically, Greenfinches were largely confined to areas of woodland or forest edge and were rarely seen in farmland or around human habitation. In some parts of continental Europe this is still the case but here, in Britain and Ireland, Greenfinches started visiting gardens in the early 1900s and are now one of the most familiar garden birds, particularly during the winter months. In addition, loose colonies of Greenfinches now feature in many urban parks and larger gardens (as well as in more rural gardens). In both cases, the planting of ornamental conifers has helped, providing the birds with excellent nesting opportunities.

The very large winter flocks that were a feature of lowland farmland during the 1940s and 1950s have diminished, with the loss of feeding opportunities provided by overwinter stubbles, full of spilt grain and weed seeds. It is perhaps fortunate then, that Greenfinches have been able to turn to gardens for food during the late winter months when alternative food sources are scarce. Results from the BTO's Garden Bird Feeding Survey have shown that Greenfinches now arrive at garden feeding stations earlier than they did 30 years ago, an indication of the difficulties they may be facing within the wider countryside.

Like other members of the finch family, Greenfinches eat a lot of seeds and their large robust bills enable them to tackle a very wide range. However, Greenfinches show some preference for seeds held within a fleshy fruit and they adore rosehips, though they may disregard the flesh and just eat the seeds. In woodland, in addition to rosehips, Greenfinches also take other large seeds: from elm and dog's mercury in summer, yew and hawthorn in autumn and bramble in winter. In farmland they take other seeds, favouring members of the crucifer and daisy families, many of which, such as charlock, are less plentiful than they used to be. In gardens, Greenfinches have exploited sunflower seeds in a big way, favouring black sunflower seed and sunflower hearts over other foods on offer. Individual birds will sit at feeders and eat a steady succession of black sunflower seeds, expertly splitting them open with their sharp-edged bills and rejecting those too small to bother with.

Although male Greenfinches may begin to sing as early in the year as January, they do not usually pair until late February or early March, with most clutches laid towards the end of April. Those birds nesting in gardens where food is provided throughout the year appear to be able to begin breeding slightly earlier than pairs elsewhere. This also means that they may be able to fit more broods into the breeding season and rear more young. Greenfinches often nest in loose colonies of 4–6 nests and the birds do not really defend clear

Female Greenfinch
by Jill Pakenham

territories in the way that most other species do. Instead, they only defend the area immediately around the nest, often foraging some distance away. This means that they will often feature at bird feeders in gardens which appear to have no suitable nesting opportunities close by. The growing young are fed on regurgitated food, made up of seeds and some insects, so you are unlikely to see adults carrying food in their bills. The nests, typically placed between 1.5 and 5m off the ground, are quite bulky and are relatively easy to find in all but the densest bushes.

Male Greenfinch by Jill Pakenham

Most of the Greenfinches that breed in Britain and Ireland are sedentary in their lifestyle, remaining close to where they were born. However, a small number move longer distances, leaving the breeding areas in autumn to winter in Ireland or departing from southeast England to winter on the Continent. These movements have aroused a great deal of interest among researchers because an individual bird may behave differently in different years. This fact, together with the timing of movements, suggests that the movements are in response to high breeding densities or food shortages during late summer, rather than a response to weather conditions. This leads to increased competition and the departure of the less competitive individuals. At the same time as these Greenfinches are departing from Britain, others (typically only a small number) are arriving from the Continent, mostly from Norway. Some of these winter visitors are believed to be birds that normally would have wintered on the Norwegian coast, while others, arriving mainly in eastern England, are birds that have drifted too far west from their usual migration route, southwards down the coast of mainland Europe. Again, at the individual level, such movements appear to be occasional rather than annual, illustrating the complexities of bird migration and the great many questions that still remain to be answered by ornithologists.

Status

Green listed. Long-term increase in gardens.

Foods

Wide range of seeds, sunflower hearts, peanuts and some insects.

Breeding

Clutch size: 4–6
Incubates: 13–14 days
Young in nest: 13–16 days
No. broods: 2–3
Season: Apr–Sep

Seasonality

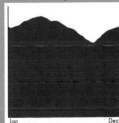

Male Greenfinches have a characteristic nasal call note, 'dzwee'. This is only likely to be confused with that uttered by the Brambling but, since the latter is a winter visitor, any nasal 'dzwee' heard during the summer is almost certainly going to be a Greenfinch. This photograph shows just how bright a male Greenfinch can appear.

Male Greenfinch by Tommy Holden

Goldfinch

Summer

Winter

The Goldfinch is a small, delicate and beautifully marked finch, its colourful plumage bright and characteristic, and its agile feeding behaviour a joy to watch. So endearing are these delightful little birds that they have proved to be very popular as cagebirds, a fashion which put great strain on the population throughout the 19th Century. Although the live-trapping of Goldfinches has been banned for many decades in Britain and Ireland, the practice still goes on in some parts of Europe, where finches are caught in automatic traps known as Chardonnerets – 'Chardonneret' also being the French word for Goldfinch.

Goldfinches are widespread within Britain and Ireland but are most abundant in lowland areas, where favoured food plants are most numerous. Many of the plant species used belong to the family Compositae and include familiar species such as dandelions, groundsels and ragworts. It is the seeds of these plants upon which the Goldfinches feed, preferring to take those that are not fully ripe but still in a milky state. This preference means that Goldfinches are quite mobile feeders, moving to new areas to find plants with seeds in a suitable state. The seasonal pattern to the Garden BirdWatch reporting rate for this species is probably influenced by the availability of different seeds. Historically, Goldfinches appear to have made use of natural foods within gardens at those times of year (especially late spring) when seed supplies in other habitats were low. In more recent years, Goldfinches have made increasing use of garden feeding stations, exploiting foods like sunflower hearts and nyjer seed. Alongside this change in feeding behaviour, we have seen an increase in the peak Garden BirdWatch reporting from 23% to 42% of gardens over an eight–year period. Goldfinches have bills that are quite long and thin, enabling them to extract seeds from plants that are typically not available to other finches. The Goldfinch is the only finch to be able to extract seeds from teasels, although even female Goldfinches find this difficult because their bills are slightly shorter than those of the males.

While the Anglo-Saxon name of 'thistle-tweaker' reflects the association between Goldfinches and thistles, the other old name of 'draw-water' has a rather different association, coming from the somewhat distasteful whimsy of training tame Goldfinches to draw up a small bucket of water on a thread as a party trick! In France and Italy, the Goldfinch had a very strong symbolic significance. It often appeared as a symbol of fertility or resurrection in early devotional paintings, sometimes placed in a prominent position within the painting but often, as in the case of 'The Nativity' by Pierro della Francesca (National Gallery, London), it is tucked away.

Goldfinches often site their nests higher off the ground than other finches, sometimes placing them in the fork of a branch up to 15m high. The nest itself is similar to that of the Chaffinch, neat and compact with a deep cup. The egg-laying

Goldfinch
by Tommy Holden

period extends from late April through to August, with young in the nest as late as September, giving many pairs the opportunity to rear two or even three broods if conditions are favourable. The developing nestlings are fed a mixture of regurgitated seeds and insects, with early broods receiving more insects than late ones, a reflection of both insect and seed abundance. Young Goldfinches lack the black, red and white

Young Goldfinch by Tommy Holden

facial markings of the adults but do show the black wings with prominent yellow bar. Some gardens may also hold nesting pairs, which defend only a very small territory around the nest site and usually feed some distance away. In urban and suburban areas, the presence of waste ground (with its many weeds) may support local breeding pairs and the increasing clean-up of such 'brownfield' sites may be reducing opportunities for Goldfinches. However, the specialisation of Goldfinches on particular plant species and their seeds may be one reason why the Goldfinch population in Britain & Ireland has not declined in the manner that other species feeding on different plant species have done.

Although Goldfinches may be seen in gardens throughout the year, many leave Britain in the autumn to winter on the Continent. These migrants do not appear to move to a specific wintering area, instead they seem to migrate south and stop once they find suitable conditions. Many Goldfinches remain within Britain and Ireland during the winter, some close to their breeding grounds while others move south or cross into Ireland. Researchers examining the sex ratios of Goldfinches remaining within Britain during the winter have produced evidence which suggests that more females migrate than males and that the females winter further south. This is a pattern also seen in some other finches, *e.g.* Chaffinch.

Keep feeding

Traditionally, garden bird feeding has stopped once the last snow and ice has gone. For the Goldfinch and other seed-eaters, April is a really important month (see the seasonality graph). By continuing to feed through the spring, you will be helping these endearing little birds at a time of the year when their other food sources are hard to find.

Goldfinch by Tommy Holden

Status
Green listed.
Increasing in gardens.

Foods
Small seeds, few insects.
Peanuts, sunflower hearts and nyjer seed.

Breeding
Clutch size: 5–6
Incubates: 12–13 days
Young in nest: 13–15 days
No. broods: 2 (3)
Season: Apr–Sep

Seasonality

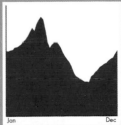

Jan   Dec

Siskin

The Siskin showed a dramatic expansion in its breeding and wintering distribution within Britain and Ireland over the course of the 20ᵗʰ Century. Breeding Siskins are associated with conifers and used to be largely restricted to Caledonian pine forests in northern Britain. However, the widespread establishment of plantation forest (notably sitka spruce) has greatly increased the amount of suitable breeding habitat. This increase in the breeding population has been matched by a change in feeding behaviour during winter. From the mid–1960s, Siskins have been recorded visiting gardens, initially feeding on fat but later learning to exploit peanuts and sunflower hearts. Prior to developing the habit of exploiting garden feeding stations, Siskins mainly wintered in alder, birch and larch woodlands, often associating with Redpolls.

It has been suggested that Siskins first moved into gardens to exploit the seeds of introduced exotic conifers, established by gardeners to provide winter greenery, and that this then led to them discovering the supplementary foods put out by garden birdwatchers. As can be seen from the annual Garden BirdWatch reporting rate, garden feeding is a feature of late winter and early spring, suggesting that the birds move into gardens once natural seed crops have been depleted. Garden feeding may also provide an advantage during early mornings or on wet or overcast days, when cones are closed and the seeds unobtainable. It is only during dry conditions that the cones open up to reveal the seeds within.

Production of seed by coniferous trees like the spruces and pines is known to vary from one year to the next. Being so dependent upon these seeds means that both Siskin breeding success and movements are determined by seed availability. In years following poor seed crops, Siskins start breeding much later in the year and rear fewer young. Variations in food availability also lead to eruptive movements of Siskins from breeding populations in the conifer forests of Scandinavia, bringing birds to Britain in varying numbers in different years. This can be seen clearly in the Garden BirdWatch reporting rate. In the winters of 1995 and 1998 the late winter peak in reporting rate showed that nearly 40% of gardens held visiting Siskins, while in most other years this value is around 15–20% (see graph).

Although some Siskins (notably those in northern regions and in Ireland) winter close to the breeding areas, many others move south to winter in central and southern Britain. At the same time, birds from Scandinavia and elsewhere in continental Europe enter Britain, either across the English Channel via

Female Siskin by Tommy Holden

Belgium and the Netherlands, or by making a direct crossing of the North Sea. Some of these birds remain here for the winter, while others pass through to wintering grounds elsewhere in Europe and North Africa. Individual birds may return to the same wintering area in successive years or may winter in widely different locations from one year to the next. Two Siskins ringed in a Surrey garden were later recaptured by a ringer in Lithuania,

Male Siskin by Tommy Holden

before reappearing in the Surrey garden two years later. One of the individuals was then found in Finland! Recent research suggests that, in some populations, individuals may adopt one of two different approaches to wintering. Some individuals settle very quickly in an area and effectively become residents, only making short-distance local movements. Others, perhaps the vast majority in some populations, become transients and are very mobile, covering large distances. Siskins visiting suburban gardens in southern Britain, often arrive in small parties and a succession of these groups will pass through individual gardens during the same day. Most Siskins will have left the gardens of southern Britain by mid-April, with birds returning surprisingly quickly to their breeding grounds. One Siskin, ringed at a site in Shropshire, was recovered in the Highland region of Scotland just three days later, thus averaging 190km per day.

Nests are usually placed high in conifers among the outer branches, making them virtually inaccessible. They are delicate in structure and hemispherical in shape, made from twigs, heather, grass and spiders' webs, woven together and lined with rootlets and hair.

Wintering Siskins

The Garden BirdWatch reporting rate for Siskin shows how the use of gardens varies between winters, depending upon the availability of tree seed.

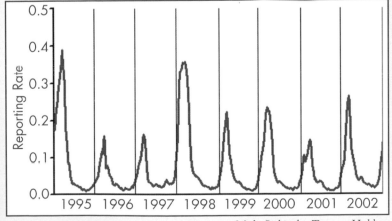

Male Siskin by Tommy Holden

Status
Green listed.
Increasing in gardens.

Foods
Seeds of conifers, alder and birch. Peanuts and sunflower hearts.

Breeding
Clutch size: 4–5
Incubates: c.12 days
Young in nest: c.15 days
No. broods: 2
Season: Apr–Aug

Seasonality

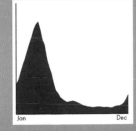

Bullfinch

Status

Red listed.

Rapid decline over last 25 years.

Foods

Seeds of fleshy fruits, buds and shoots. Some insects.

Breeding

Clutch size: 4–6

Incubates: 12–14 days

Young in nest: 12–16 days

No. broods: 2

Season: Apr–Sep

Seasonality

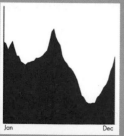

Jan   Dec

Despite their characteristic and striking appearance, Bullfinches are relatively shy birds. Breeding pairs occupy a range of habitats, characterised by the presence of dense bushes in which they nest, and are found across much of Britain and Ireland. They are absent as a breeding species from the Isle of Man, the Western Isles, Orkney and Shetland.

Between the 1950s and mid-1970s, Bullfinches were abundant across much of southern Britain, in some areas becoming a serious pest of commercial fruit trees. This led to licensed control of the birds, something which seems to have had no significant effects on population size. The more recent decline in numbers, highlighted by BTO survey work, is thought to be the result of changing agricultural practices and the loss of arable weeds. Culling of Bullfinches has now virtually ceased as the species is no longer the pest it once was.

Bullfinches turn to the buds of fruiting trees in late winter and early spring, when supplies of tree seeds, especially ash, run low. Flower buds are preferred to leaf buds because they are nutritionally more rewarding. Selection of cultivated varieties over uncultivated varieties occurs because Man has selectively bred the cultivated varieties to give a higher yield, making them more appealing to the Bullfinches. At other times of the year, the birds feed on the seeds of ash, elm, nettle, dock and dog's mercury, among others, only taking insects when feeding young during part of the breeding season. The Bullfinch appears slower and more deliberate than other finches when feeding. Individuals can be seen manipulating seeds and buds in the bill, turning food items with the tongue and removing the pulp against the lower mandible before swallowing the seeds. The birds prefer to feed on the plant, and often leave the skin and pulpy flesh of a fruit hanging, having removed the seeds. In recent years they have started to utilise seed feeders, taking black sunflower and other seeds. The Garden BirdWatch reporting rate peaks in mid-summer, when the demands of hungry chicks may bring family parties to garden feeding stations.

Both adults and young appear to be remarkably sedentary in their habits, typically remaining in the vicinity of a good food supply, including sunflower hearts in hanging feeders, for long periods.

Bullfinch pairs appear to be long-lasting, with individuals remaining together from one breeding season to the next. Established pairs do not seem to be overly territorial during the breeding season, perhaps because of the low density at which they occur.

Male Bullfinch by Rosie Rees

While the Yellowhammer is a familiar bird of farmland and open country, it is only a very occasional visitor to gardens, typically appearing in rural gardens during periods of severe winter weather or during late spring when natural food supplies are at their lowest. Yellowhammers are most abundant in central and eastern Britain, while in Ireland they are now restricted mainly to the south and east of the country. This distribution reflects the Yellowhammer's preference for areas of tilled land used for the production of cereals. Yellowhammers predominantly feed on the seeds of grasses and cereals, preferring these starchy seeds to those rich in oils (such as the crucifers), hence the association with arable farmland.

Even outside the breeding season, Yellowhammers remain within farmland, congregating with other seed-eaters on stubbles or game-cover strips. Hedgerows are important during the breeding season because the species nests low down in hedge bases, but there also need to be some taller shrubs, trees or telephone wires from which the characteristic song can be delivered. This has been immortalised in the phrase '*a little bit of bread and no chee-eese*' and remains one of the most familiar farmland sounds.

It is well known that many species of farmland bird began long-term declines in the 1970s, coinciding with a period of significant change in the way in which agriculture was practised across much of lowland Britain. Intriguingly, the Yellowhammer population appears to have been stable over the early part of this period, not beginning its own steady decline until the late 1980s. Analysis of BTO ringing data suggests that the survival rates of adult Yellowhammers have declined over this period, something which may be linked to reduced food availability during the winter or spring months. It might be possible to examine this further by using information from the BTO Garden Bird Feeding Survey, to see if Yellowhammers have made increasing use of rural gardens during the period of decline within farmland.

The Garden BirdWatch reporting rate for Yellowhammer now peaks at 8% of rural gardens during late spring, a fall from 12% just eight years ago, when Garden BirdWatch was launched.

Summer

Winter

Status
Red listed.
Widespread decline.

Foods
Seeds, especially those rich in starch, insects in breeding season.

Breeding
Clutch size: 3–5
Incubates: 12–14 days
Young in nest: 12–13 days
No. broods: 2–3
Season: Apr–Sep

Yellowhammers have a yellow head and chestnut brown rump, with chestnut fringes to the brown wing feathers. The males (photo) are far more striking than the females, the latter sex often appearing drab and only faintly yellow. The chisel-shaped bill is typical of a seed-eater and the bird is about the size of a sparrow.

Yellowhammer by Tommy Holden

Seasonality

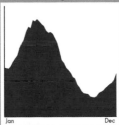

Reed Bunting

Status

Red listed.
Declining in all habitats.

Foods

Seeds and other plant material, insects.

Breeding

Clutch size: 4–5
Incubates: 13–14 days
Young in nest: 10–13 days
No. broods: 2 (3)
Season: May–Sep

Seasonality

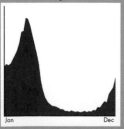

Jan   Dec

The Reed Bunting is a scarce visitor to gardens, only tending to occur in rural gardens during winter or late spring. Reed Buntings breed in a wide variety of habitats, not just the damp one suggested by the name. In fact, Reed Buntings can be found breeding among the marram grass of sand dune systems, in farm hedgerows and even within fields planted with oil seed rape. The use of drier habitats is relatively recent, possibly a consequence of the loss of damp habitats to agricultural intensification or because of the decline in Yellowhammer abundance (a potential competitor within drier habitats). Unlike the Yellowhammer, the Reed Bunting does not need tall shrubs and trees from which to proclaim its territorial rights. Instead, it will readily sing from the stem of a reed or dock just protruding above the surrounding vegetation.

Reed Bunting populations in lowland Britain have shown a similar pattern of decline to many other small seed-eating birds. Although Reed Buntings are almost exclusively insectivorous during the breeding season, they quickly revert to feeding on seeds in late summer. It seems likely that their decline is in part due to a lack of available seeds during the winter months. Evidence in support of this hypothesis comes from the Garden Bird Feeding Survey, which revealed a major increase in the use made of gardens by Reed Buntings during the period of decline for farmland populations. Although it is known that severe winter weather can have a significant impact on Reed Bunting populations, this effect is short-lived and recovery from weather-related declines happens quickly. It is during the winter months that large flocks of Reed Buntings often gather together to roost, using wet or marshy areas and reedbeds, where they will be able to spend the night away from likely predators. During the day, these roosts break up and the birds forage widely over farmland and waste ground, in search of weed seeds and spilt cereal grain.

Reed Buntings have a long breeding season and eggs can be laid from early May, typically in a well-concealed nest positioned low down in the vegetation. The vast majority of British and Irish Reed Buntings remain here in the winter and are joined by a very small number of birds from Scandinavia.

Reed Buntings may be missed in winter. The characteristic black head and white collar of the breeding male (main photo) are hidden behind brown feather tips that will gradually be worn away in spring to reveal the striking breeding plumage. Females are less boldly marked (inset)

Reed Buntings by Tommy Holden

One of the great joys of birdwatching is discovering a bird that is new to you, especially if this is in your own 'patch'. To find out what it is you will need to look at a bird book or ask a friend. It is helpful if you can make sure that you are looking out for key identification features. This is where an understanding of bird design comes in.

All garden birds follow a basic body plan, slightly adapted to a particular way of life in each individual species. Understanding this basic plan, and becoming familiar with the terminology used to name the different parts of a bird, is an important first step in being able to identify particular species. Many of the guide books use this terminology and it is helpful when taking notes to use the terms as outlined in the diagram below.

Various features (see box – right) can be used to help in the identification process but don't expect to be able to identify every bird that you see, especially if you only have a brief view. As birdwatchers, we are always learning and refining our identification skills.

Things to look for

Size: Note the size of the bird relative to any familiar species that may be alongside it – is it about the size of a Blackbird or a House Sparrow?

Bill: Look at the shape of the bill – is it thin and pointed like a Robin or more wedge-shaped like that of a finch or sparrow?

Shape: Does the bird have a long tail, long legs or a big head?

What is it doing?: Does the bird hop or walk? Does it flick its wings (like a Dunnock) or its tail (like a Pied Wagtail)?

Colour: Surprisingly, colours are not necessarily the best features, as appearance may vary with light and weather conditions. Good things to look for include white feathers in the tail or wing, patterns around the eye and the colour of the head, throat and breast.

Voice: Is the song similar to a bird you know well? What is the call-note like – the 'tack' of a Robin or the 'wheeze' of a Greenfinch?

Naming the parts

When describing a bird you cannot identify to somebody else it is helpful to use a standard system to name the parts of the bird's plumage. Some of the most commonly used names are shown on this diagram, although there are many others - most notably in relation to patterns on the head. Look out for a stripe through the eye (as shown here), an eye-ring, moustachial stripes and whether there is an 'eyebrow' (called the supercilium).

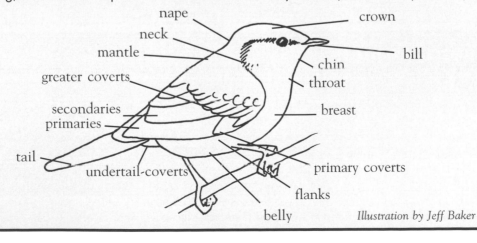

nape • neck • mantle • greater coverts • secondaries • primaries • tail • undertail-coverts • crown • bill • chin • throat • breast • primary coverts • flanks • belly

Illustration by Jeff Baker

Pigeons and doves

Collared Dove

More delicate than the pigeons, with a slim build. Collared Doves have pale grey underparts and pinkish buff upperparts. The eye, which is red in breeding adults, is surrounded by a white eye ring. Adults have a black neck collar, finely edged with white, which is perhaps the best feature for use in identification. The song is characteristic and made up of three notes 'coo-coo-cuh' with emphasis on the second phrase.

Collared Dove by Tommy Holden (c.f. pages 54–55)

Woodpigeon

This is our largest pigeon, and is noticeably bigger than both Feral Pigeon and Stock Dove. The overall appearance is of a large, round–bellied bird, with a pink breast and grey upperparts. The main wing feathers and tip of the tail are black, and there is a white neck patch present in the adult, above which there is an iridescent green patch. Both of these are lacking in young birds. The song of 'hooh-hrooo' is usually uttered with a characteristic rhythm.

Woodpigeon by Tommy Holden (c.f. page 53)

Stock Dove

Reminiscent of a slimmed-down Woodpigeon. The grey tones of the upperparts are stronger in their colouration, although the rump is a paler grey. The main wing feathers and tip of the tail (which is shorter than in Woodpigeon) are black. The breast is pink and the belly an off-white. The iridescent green neck patch is larger than in Woodpigeon and there is no white neck patch (note that a young Woodpigeon also lacks the white patch). Birds of all ages show a very short, black, double wing bar.

Stock Dove by Tommy Holden

Feral Pigeon

Feral Pigeons come in a very wide range of colour forms, although often dark grey across the back and wings. All white or all black individuals are often seen among the large city centre flocks. Most individuals have some green or purple sheen on the neck and some black barring on the wings. A white eye ring and bright orange eye are visible at close range. Some birds resemble the true wild Rock Dove from which they are descended, but these usually lack the white rump that is seen in the Rock Dove.

Feral Pigeon by John Tully (c.f. page 52)

Song Thrush

Smaller than a Blackbird, with generally warm-brown upperparts.

At 20–24 cm in length, the Song Thrush is smaller than a Blackbird, slightly larger than a Redwing and about 15% smaller than a Mistle Thrush. Song Thrushes usually have warm-brown upperparts but some individuals show colder tones, more akin to those seen on the Mistle Thrush. The underparts are predominantly white, with a warm-brown/buff wash on the sides, which extends and strengthens in colour under the wing. The brown spots on the underparts tend to be arranged in lines on the flanks.

The tail is proportionally shorter than in the Mistle Thrush and lacks any obvious white colouration. Song Thrushes are usually seen alone or in pairs, feeding on the ground. The flight is fast and direct and may be accompanied by a short call-note. The song consists of a series of vigorous, simple phrases, less rich than that of a Blackbird. Each phrase of the song is usually repeated two or three times.

Song Thrushes by Tommy Holden.

Mistle Thrush

A large, stocky thrush, bigger than a Blackbird, with pale grey-brown upperparts and heavily spotted below.

At 26–29 cm in length, the Mistle Thrush is one of our larger thrushes, being slightly larger than a Blackbird and noticeably larger than a Song Thrush. It often appears more plump-bellied than a Song Thrush and has a proportionally longer tail. When on the ground, the Mistle Thrush often adopts an upright stance that further emphasises its size.

The upperparts are a pale grey-brown and the white underparts are heavily spotted. These spots do not form lines on the flank but may form a necklace pattern around the throat. The underwings are white, which contrasts with the colour seen in the Song Thrush. The long tail has distinctive white tips to the outer feathers. Often seen in the open in small family groups and more boisterous in nature than its smaller cousin. Mistle Thrushes utter a series of harsh chattering notes (a rattling call), particularly when alarmed or disturbed.

Mistle Thrushes by Tommy Holden (top) and Phil Farrer (bottom)

Great Tit

The Great Tit is the largest of our tits and is also one of the least agile, spending a lot of time on the ground. Adults have a black and white head, with a green-blue back and blue and white wings. Young birds are similar, though less strongly marked and with pale lemon yellow cheeks in place of the white seen in adults. The breast and belly are lemon yellow, with a black central stripe running down its length. The stripe is wider in males than in females.

Great Tit by Tommy Holden (c.f. pages 92–93)

Blue Tit

The Blue Tit is about 20% smaller than a Great Tit and has a blue crown, wing feathers and tail. The face has white cheeks and a white stripe above each eye (these areas of white are pale yellow in young birds). The underparts are lemon yellow and lack the wide black stripe seen in Great Tits. Blue Tits are agile birds, familiar to most garden birdwatchers. They can often be heard uttering their churring alarm calls.

Blue Tit by Tommy Holden (c.f. pages 90–91)

Coal Tit

Coal Tits can be identified by the white stripe running down the nape, set against a black cap and bib. About the same size as a Blue Tit, these agile little birds have a pale toffee belly and breast and olive-grey or brown upperparts. Coal Tits have two white wing bars (see photograph), both of which are absent in the Marsh and Willow Tit, with which Coal Tit could possibly be confused.

Coal Tit by Tommy Holden (c.f. pages 88–89)

Marsh/Willow Tit

These two birds are similar in their appearance, although there are subtle differences that can be used to separate them. The Marsh Tit has a glossy black cap and a small black bib. In the Willow Tit, the cap is a dull black and the bib is more extensive. While the upperparts of both birds are a plain brown colour, the Willow Tit has pale fringes to its secondaries, which gives the appearance of a pale wing panel. The calls are diagnostic - 'zi zi taah taah taah' in Willow and 'pichou' in Marsh.

Marsh Tit by Tommy Holden (c.f. pages 86-87)

Carrion Crow

The Carrion Crow can be separated from the Rook by its heavy black bill. This appears blunter than that of the Rook, curving most towards the tip. The shape of the head is another useful feature, appearing flatter on the crown. The overall appearance is of a more compact bird which lacks the shaggy thighs of the Rook. Both Rook and Carrion Crow are noticeably smaller than the Raven, which has a very heavy and powerful bill, together with a shaggy throat.

Carrion Crow by Mike Weston (c.f. page 101)

Rook

In adult Rooks, the whitish base to the bill, steep forehead and pointed bill are characteristic. In young birds, lacking the white base to the bill, the other features can still be seen, especially the pointed bill – this tapers along its length to a sharp point. The feathers on the flanks appear loose, especially when the bird is striding across the ground. Rooks are generally more gregarious than Crows. They utter a range of calls but perhaps the most familiar is the rather flat sounding 'kaah'.

Rook by George Higginbotham (c.f. page 100)

Jackdaw

The Jackdaw is a small crow, about the size of a pigeon, with a short bill. Adult birds have a grey nape and grey sides to the head, which contrast with the black cap and bib. Adults also have an obviously pale eye during the breeding season. Young birds are duller in colouration than their parents (see photograph). Jackdaws are sociable birds, often seen in gardens or perched at the entrances to their nests in tree cavities or within chimneys.

Adult Jackdaw (left) with young by John Harding (c.f. page 99)

Raven

The Raven is the largest of our crows and is only an occasional garden visitor, largely restricted to visiting rural gardens in the north and west of Britain. The Raven is a much bigger bird than either the Rook or Carrion Crow and the smallest Ravens are still bigger than the largest Carrion Crows. The overall appearance is of a much stockier, more heavily built bird, with a heavy bill and noticeably shaggy throat feathers. In flight, the wedge-shaped tail is characteristic.

Raven by Tommy Holden

House Sparrow

A small but stocky bird, somewhat scruffy in appearance and colonial in nature.

The House Sparrow is a small bird, with a stout bill designed for eating seeds. At 14–16 cm in length, the House Sparrow is larger than the Tree Sparrow, though this difference is unlikely to be obvious in the field. Adult males are distinctive, the crown and nape are grey and only the sides of the head are brown. The wide black bib extends down onto the chest. The back is warm brown, streaked with black but with a few white wing feathers.

Adult females and juvenile birds of both sexes are a light sandy brown in colour with brown and grey streaks on the back and wings.

House Sparrows make a range of chirping calls; the courtship song being rather unkindly described as a monotonous series of the chirp call note. These communal birds like to feed from thick cover, venturing out to feeders sited within four or five metres of the available bushes.

Female House Sparrow (top) by Darren Frost and male House Sparrow (bottom) by Mike Weston.

Tree Sparrow

This species is more likely to visit rural gardens than those in built-up areas.

Both male and female Tree Sparrows are of similar appearance and can be distinguished from House Sparrows by differences in the colour of the plumage on and around the head. Tree Sparrows have a characteristic warm red-brown crown, white patches to the sides of the head and a small black cheek patch. There is also a narrow white collar. The black bib is much smaller than that seen in a male House Sparrow, reaching only the top of the chest and narrow in outline. Juvenile birds are similar in appearance to the adults but are duller in colour and have dark rather than white cheeks. They still have the warm red-brown cap.

Tree Sparrows are loosely colonial in nature, forming small flocks during summer. In winter, much larger flocks occur, often with finches and House Sparrows. The calls are rather similar to those uttered by the House Sparrow but richer in tone, with a distinctive 'tsuwitt'.

Tree Sparrow by Rosie Rees

Chaffinch

Both male and female Chaffinches have black and white wings and an olive green rump. The male has a pinky-red breast and cheeks, and steel blue crown and nape. These colours are most pronounced during the breeding season – during winter they are more subdued. Females and juveniles are plainer in colouration, light grey/brown above with a hint of green. When seen in flight, the white feathers in the outer edges of the tail and the white wing bar are often visible.

Male Chaffinch by Tommy Holden (c.f. pages 108–109)

Brambling

Bramblings (of all ages and sexes) have a white rump and this, together with the lack of any white edges to the tail makes a very useful identification feature. The orange-brown shoulders and breast can be seen in both sexes but are more pronounced in the male. The glossy blue-black head colour of the male is a breeding season feature. In winter, grey tips to the crown feathers obscure the black beneath. Females have a grey-brown head but are still brighter than a female Chafinch.

Female Brambling by Tommy Holden (c.f. page 107)

Greenfinch

Male Greenfinches are a dull olive-green, with greenish-yellow on the breast and rump, together with bright yellow wing patches and yellow to the edge of the tail. Females and immatures are duller in appearance, with less yellow visible in the plumage. Recently fledged birds are paler still, with streaked plumage. On dull winter days, individuals can appear very drab (almost brown in colour) but the yellow wing flashes are obvious in flight. Similar in size to a House Sparrow they are bigger than a Siskin.

Male Greenfinch by Tommy Holden (c.f. pages 110–111)

Siskin

The Siskin is smaller than a Goldfinch and much smaller than a Greenfinch. The plumage is predominantly a yellow-green colour, with a striking yellow band on the wing and yellow patches at the base of the tail. Adult males have a black crown and a lot of black in the wing. Females are greyer in colour, streaked above and without the black crown. Juveniles resemble females but are buff-brown above and more heavily streaked (both above and below).

Male Siskin by Tommy Holden (c.f. page 114–115)

Further reading

There is a wide range of information available on garden birds and wildlife-friendly gardening, in books or magazines, on videos and cd-roms or on the internet. A few of the best sources of information, together with some useful addresses, are given below.

Books

Bill Oddie's Introduction to Birdwatching. Bill Oddie. 144pp. Hardback. New Holland. ISBN 1 85974 894 5.

Collins Bird Guide. Killian Mullarney, Lars Svensson, Dan Zetterström & Peter Grant. 392pp. Hardback. ISBN 0 00219 728 6.

Attracting Birds to your Garden. Stephen Moss & David Cottridge. 160pp. Paperback. New Holland. ISBN 1 85974 005 7.

The Birdwatcher's Garden. Hazel Johnson & Pamela Johnson. 168pp. Paperback. Guild of Master Craftsman Publications. ISBN 1 86108 135 9.

The State of the Nations' Birds. Chris Mead. 252pp. Paperback. Whittet Books. ISBN 1 873580 45 2.

Garden BirdWatch Handbook. Andrew Canon. 80pp. Paperback. British Trust for Ornithology. ISBN 0 90379 398 9.

The BTO NestBox Guide. Chris du Feu. 80pp. Paperback. British Trust for Ornithology. ISBN 1 902576 81 0. Due Spring 2004.

The Wildlife Pond Handbook. Louise Bardsley. 80pp. Paperback. New Holland. ISBN 1 84330 111 3.

Bird food and feeders

A wide range of foods, feeders, nestboxes and other products for wildlife-friendly gardening are available from: CJ WildBird Foods Ltd, The Rea, Upton Magna, Shrewsbury, Shropshire, SY4 4UR. Telephone 0800–731–2820 or visit their website at www.birdfood.co.uk.

Compact disks and tapes

Garden Bird Sounds. Compact Disk. ISBN 1 89866 576 1.

Teach Yourself Bird Sounds. Number 1. Garden birds. Tape.

The Video Guide to Garden Birds. The DVD Video Guide to Garden Birds. The CD-ROM Guide to Garden Birds. All three titles are published by BirdGuides and are available from CJ WildBird Foods.

Useful addresses

British Trust for Ornithology, The Nunnery, Thetford, Norfolk, IP24 2PU. www.bto.org. Tel: 01842–750050.

BTO Scotland, School of Biological and Environmental Sciences, Cottrell Building, University of Stirling, Stirling, FK9 4LA. Tel: 01786–466560.

The Mammal Society, 2B, Inworth Street, London, SW11 3EP. Tel: 020–7350–2200.

Bat Conservation Trust, 15 Cloisters House, 8 Battersea Park Road, London, SW8 4BG. Tel: 020–7627–2629.

Froglife, Triton House, Bramfield, Halesworth, Suffolk, IP19 9AE. Tel: 01986–784518.

Butterfly Conservation, Manor Yard, East Lulworth, Wareham, Dorset, BH20 5QP. Tel: 01929–400209.

Plantlife, 14 Rollestone Street, Salisbury, Wiltshire, SP1 1DX. Tel: 01722–342730.

Each of the individual species accounts contains a standard set of information on status, regional use of gardens, breeding ecology and seasonality. This information is presented as a series of maps, notes and graphs, each of which is explained in this key (right). This information comes form a number of BTO surveys, most notably from Garden BirdWatch itself, and includes new information on the use of gardens across regions (the maps) and season (the seasonality graph).

Regional use of gardens

The use made of gardens in different parts of Britain and Ireland is shown on two maps, one for the summer Garden BirdWatch quarter (July–September) and one for winter (January–March). Garden BirdWatch reporting rates are shown for each of the following regions: North Scotland, South Scotland, Wales, Ireland, Northeast England, Northwest England, Yorkshire & Humberside, East Midlands, West Midlands, East of England, Southeast England, Southwest England and London. The colours used on the map respresent the following reporting rate categories:

0–1%	2–5%	6–30%
31–60%	61–80%	81–100%

Status

The current conservation status of the species is shown, following the listing approach described on page 27. Green-listed species are regarded as being of low conservation concern (their populations are stable or increasing), Amber-listed species are of medium conservation concern, while Red-listed species are of high conservation concern. The general trend in how the population has changed is noted. In many cases this specifically refers to the trend in gardens, as revealed by the BTO's Garden Bird Feeding Survey.

Foods

The main foods normally taken by the species are listed, often with reference to supplementary foodstuffs that may be taken at garden feeding stations.

Breeding

Information on the usual number of eggs in a clutch, the length of the incubation period, the length of time that chicks remain in the nest, the number of breeding attempts made during the course of the breeding season and the length of the breeding season are all derived from information gathered through the BTO's Nest Record Scheme.

Seasonality graph

See overleaf.

Summer

Winter

Status
Green list. The Carrion Crow has increased steadily since the 1960s.

Foods
Invertebrates, cereal grain, eggs, carrion and scraps.

Breeding
Clutch size: 4–6
Incubates: c.19 days
Young in nest: 26–35 days
No. broods: 1
Season: Mar–Jul

Seasonality

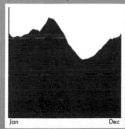

Jan   Dec

Seasonality graph

The seasonality graph presents information on the use of Garden BirdWatch gardens throughout the year. The vertical axis represents the Garden BirdWatch reporting rate, although no scale is shown, each graph being scaled individually to show the pattern of use in a readable manner. In order to allow the reader to establish how great the use of gardens is for any species, the actual Garden BirdWatch reports rates are shown in the following table. For each of the main Garden BirdWatch species, the reporting rate is given as a percentage, allowing comparisons to be made between seasons and between species. Further information appears on the Garden BirdWatch web pages and in issues of the *Bird Table*.

	Jan–Mar	Apr–Jun	Jul–Sep	Oct–Dec
Blackbird	97	97	86	89
Blackcap	11	6	3	4
Black-headed Gull	7	2	2	5
Blue Tit	96	92	88	94
Brambling	4	1	<1	1
Bullfinch	7	8	5	4
Carrion Crow	27	29	21	24
Chaffinch	82	76	62	71
Coal Tit	47	34	36	56
Collared Dove	76	79	75	70
Dunnock	81	76	64	73
Feral Pigeon	11	13	11	10
Fieldfare	4	<1	<1	3
Goldcrest	6	4	3	6
Goldfinch	21	27	14	15
Great Spotted Woodpecker	19	22	19	19
Great Tit	80	76	74	81
Greenfinch	76	79	69	68
House Sparrow	77	82	78	76
Jackdaw	22	29	18	19
Jay	11	12	10	14
Long-tailed tit	27	11	9	15
Magpie	52	55	47	55
Marsh/Willow Tit	6	4	4	6
Mistle Thrush	9	9	4	7
Nuthatch	12	10	13	13
Pied Wagtail	13	10	7	11
Redwing	6	<1	<1	4
Reed Bunting	2	1	<1	<1
Robin	92	78	75	90
Rook	10	12	6	7
Siskin	15	7	2	2
Song Thrush	34	36	23	18
Sparrowhawk	10	8	10	11
Starling	74	76	57	62
Tawny Owl	3	2	3	3
Tree Sparrow	5	5	4	4
Treecreeper	3	1	1	2
Woodpigeon	56	67	59	46
Wren	42	32	31	41
Yellowhammer	3	4	2	1